Confessions of a Black Travel DIVA

Stories of a Brown Girl and a Suitcase

Tatiana Yvette Smith

STARCHILD  PUBLICATIONS

For Bella, my best story ever.

Dear God,
If I die today, I just want to say Thank You
because I've had a fabulous life.

LONG ISLAND

I felt a gentle nudge on my shoulder as my grandmother called my name in her deep raspy voice. It was still dark outside as I wobbled out of the bed into the car, my pajamas still on and sleep in my eyes. It was my grandma and I, once again, partners on the road, as we gathered speed along the Long Island Expressway in search of the world. No one could stop us. It was amazing that my mother had enough trust in her own mother to allow her to drive cross-country with me, a 5-year-old, bursting with energy and an insatiable curiosity. But then again, my mother was a young mother, who, having had me at nineteen and being married and divorced in the same year, was still looking for freedom and excitement in her own life.

Grandma was still grand at the time. She was curvy, flirtatious, and spontaneous. A thick black woman, she not only survived the Great Depression, but bore witness to the unfathomable, in the backwoods of Jim Crow-era Texas, the free-loving '60s, the coke-filled '70's, and now, their destructive aftermath in the '80s. She had just begun wearing wigs, full of bountiful, rich chocolate curls and the magic that I knew as her bountiful hair was now both demystified and surreal. She still powdered herself, even on those long trips, and the faint smell of Chanel N° 5 permeated the plush velvet car seats. She would gaze at me, and then at the road, through her oversized pink and beige-colored frames. The two of us were larger than life. The road was ours.

My grandmother took to the road freely, with a fierce drive and steely determination that came from being the wife of a philandering, alcoholic husband who would disappear for weeks on end while indulging in his own whims. Grandma took this as an opportunity not to wallow in her misery but to live a life of uninhibited choices. She chose to buy her own car and drive.

We drove along small roads, big roads, and rough, gravelly roads, in her hefty silver '85 Riviera that sped alongside the fastest sports cars inside tunnels that spanned state lines. The night would gradually turn into day and then days, so that the hazy blur of small towns and hills and cows were a part of the ride that was serene and mostly forgettable. We passed through hot states, lush green states, hilly states, flat states, and states with only white people in them. We passed through mountains and valleys and deep, deep canyons. Sometimes we would stop and sleep in a motel, or more often in the Riviera.

We passed flat, grassy fields studded with cows, and dry dirt roads with cow carcasses. At one point we passed what I thought was a volcano, with a dark cloud hovering above. I remember shrieking at what I believed was a real eruption, only to be let down when she, all-knowing grandma, told me that it was just a coincidental meeting of land and sky. Sometimes, I would hang my head outside the window and open my mouth wide to gulp in the air whole as the sun bathed my brown face and my braided, wiry pigtails waved wildly in the wind.

I had just begun to understand the difference between the foreign and the native. Long Island's South Shore, Robert Moses Park, and sea salt were native. The North Shore, rocky parks, and quaint villages were foreign, but these road warrior days with grandma where I popped my head under smoke-filled teepees with real Indians in them were far away from my "native" land. These days were filled with uncharted destinations, filled with the adventures that I dreamed about from my cozy suburban home.

It was one particular trip that held strong in the emerging mold of my young mind. My grandmother and I had embarked on yet another drive across state lines that took us to the Deep South. One day the driving stopped; my grandmother looked at me and let out a long sigh. "We're here." Where here was, I wasn't sure, but it was warm and welcoming. She would later tell me that we had made it to California in a record time of one week. I don't recall much of what California was like, except that it was exceptionally warm. My grandmother mentioned something about a theme park, where lots of little children love to go, and she promised we would make it there, but first, we needed to stop for a rest. By the time she tired of driving, it was nearly nightfall. Realizing that we would have to find a hotel soon, she stopped at the brightest, most occupied hotel with a sign of a vacancy. We were delighted to find a pool there.

"Let's have a swim," she suggested. We went into our budget hotel room and I emerged from the bathroom in an unmemorable, one-piece bathing suit, ready for my underwater adventures. We walked together to the pool where there were several families playing together in the water I looked at my grandmother and she pushed me towards the pool, encouraging me to play by myself with the other children. I waded cautiously in the water. It was evening and the lights above the pool reflected onto the water. Suddenly, a heavy hand grabbed me from behind and pushed me under the water. I blinked twice beneath the surface, while being held down by the unknown force. I heard someone tell me to blow out of my mouth like I was blowing into a straw. I emerged blurry-eyed and breathless, and looked to my grandmother for comfort and reassurance. She stood there at the edge of the pool, and watched me as I flailed my arms and legs back and forth in fear of drowning.

"Keep going," she yelled. "You'll get it. You don't need anybody to hold your hand. Do it by yourself." My five-year-old eyes stared at her in disbelief at the thought that the one person who could save me would abandon me. I flailed around in circles, horrified until somebody, a stranger in the pool, offered me some sage advice. "Put your feet down. On the bottom of the pool." Why flail around when I could stand firmly? The reasoning was so simple, and yet, at the time, I couldn't process the concept of standing firmly on my own without having to splash around uncontrollably. If I wasn't able to float, I could just stand. And when I was ready to try floating again, the fall wouldn't be so far, or so I had hoped.

The women in my life have always been fierce advocates of independence, while birthing children with the help of various men in their lives to support them. Yet, their paths always seemed to return to the traditional ideas of success, which was ultimately a comfortable home. This life—the endless cycle of bearing children, cooking, and cleaning—was a nightmare vision for me- a death-in life. My grandmother, who had spent all of her youth floating her way through this nightmare, just to be able to make it, was finally taking a stand in this new stage of her life, where she embraced a new sense of freedom. I wanted this same freedom, without ever having to embrace the nightmare. I loathed the static future of a life heavily dependent on a Prince Charming. I wanted a taste of the good life, on my own terms, with the men that I chose, and the money from my own pockets, with the freedom to come and go as I pleased. I would ultimately- find this life, and come to love and resent it through the various passions that would engulf me throughout my lifetime.

~

My next travel excursion not only took me across nations, but across seas. It was my mother who took me to get my first passport, a document that would give me access to worlds unseen by my friends and family. I was about seven years old when my mother and I boarded a late-night international flight in springtime. I knew nothing of this place called London that my mother spoke so wistfully about, other than the fact that my aunt and uncle lived there. We would stay with Elaine, my mother's best friend, once we arrived. Elaine had come from London to the New Jersey suburbs to work as a professional female butler for a wealthy family in Englewood Cliffs. My mother had dreamed about the English countryside, and the British, with their accents and cloudy afternoons scented with tea, kettles steaming with anything from Earl Grey and English Breakfast to Darjeeling. I knew nothing of these things. And so we went to this cold place and toured castles, musty dungeons in those ruined castles, bad food, endless rain, punk rock bands with colorful mohawks and colorful gardens throughout the English countryside. I'm not sure if I understood the magnitude of it all--this was a new place, a new adventure, but I wasn't sure how it would impact my suburban life back home.

My mother was bold. Five months pregnant with my sister, she took the trip, crossing an ocean to visit her dreams in person. My memories of this first trip are both vivid and vague. I remember tasting my first newspaper-wrapped fish and chips in a London ghetto, a crispy, greasy snack that satiated our hungry stomachs, as we seemed to never be able to find anything good to eat. The memories come in bits and pieces. I remember walking across Wembley Stadium hurriedly, in the rain, to my uncle's house, which lie on the other side. I remember staring at a guard under London Bridge who wouldn't smile despite my comedic antics. I remember high tea and scones and clotted cream, of which Elaine took the pleasure of introducing me. My most vivid memories of London seemed to revolve around teatime.

My mother's friend, Elaine, had arranged for an intimate tea at the historic Lanesborough Hotel on the edge of Hyde Park. My mother and I were to arrive at precisely 4pm to indulge in an array of delicately carved finger sandwiches, teas, cakes, and the finest cookies, while being waited upon by the hotel's top wait staff. I was intrigued. My mother seized upon the opportunity to teach me a lesson of grace.

We sat in the imposing dining room among the plush table arrangement, two black girls amongst a sea of white British women with old money. The table setting was overwhelming, and my mother quietly instructed me on which fork and plate to use first, and why it was not lady-like to scrape my spoon against the bottom of the teacup. I had remarked that some of the gentlemen in the room were doing just that.

"Ignore them," she said. "They don't know any better. They're savages. Gently sway your spoon back and forth in the tea. Back and forth. Back and forth. Don't let the spoon hit the cup. Don't make a sound. Back and forth."

~

The European streets we passed and the trains and journeys we took to get to our destinations were vague, but the people were not. I have an affinity for recalling faces and visual stimulation that I could exercise with a stroke of a crayon or a pen against a piece of Moleskin paper. I would come home from these trips, elated, exhausted, and a little confused. My classmates and teachers would clamor around me as I told them stories of foreign lands and showed pictures of guards in bright red suits and straight faces.

I knew I was doing things that a lot of my classmates weren't but I just didn't understand the enormity of it. For my young mind, the exciting part was going on a plane and getting the goody bags especially reserved for young jetsetters like me. But I could never imagine that those little seeds—a car trip across America, visits to London and Paris—would take me to places of pleasure and pain that I could never conjure in my wildest dreams. These stories are the confessions of a black travel diva.

~

My father was the hardest-working man I knew. He came to the United States in the 1970's as a young Haitian boy in search of the American dream, and though he was exposed to a life of excess, he lived life simply. My father spent days, nights and weekends working overtime as a design engineer creating medical footwear, so that I could have everything I could ever want or need. When I told him that I had chosen an art school in New York City over the prestigious Ivy League college of which I had been accepted, he was disappointed, but ultimately supportive. My father would buy hundreds of dollars of art supplies, without question, as I trudged through art school, while I balanced life as a dependent teenager trying to learn to be a responsible young adult.

I spent my college years at an art school, taking random classes in sewing and furniture making and blowing through my father's hard-earned cash for art supplies. I was an aimless student, wandering the city streets for the next big thing. I knew I wanted a career in art, but in art school I was overwhelmed with so many endless possibilities that I almost ended up accomplishing nothing at all. When my tab for tuition began hovering at a little over $50,000 after a three semesters I knew I had to get serious and settle on a major in design. Still, this nagging thought didn't keep me from traveling. I supplemented my plane tickets and Pearl Paint shopping sprees with the money I made from my customer service job at Kozmo.com, an Internet service delivering DVD's, Cosi sandwiches and Ben & Jerry's within an hour with the stroke of an iMac key. I was pulling fifty-five-hour shifts on top of my full-time school schedule. When I wasn't in school or at work, I spent my time buried in travel magazines and the Destinations section of the *New York Times*.

The times I spent in those school years were wild and obnoxious, as I sought to navigate my new independence in the big city as a former suburbanite. By then I had moved from a monotonous Long Island village to the harsher streets of Brooklyn, where I took up residence in the brownstones of various neighborhoods. My days were a world of art, deadlines, and intellectual stimulation, while my nights were full of an excess of everything that I couldn't or shouldn't have had. I would often roam Alphabet City in my skimpy attire that I had bought only hours earlier from lower Broadway, looking for trouble. I eventually found a comrade at Kozmo.com. Shing-I, one of my first true friends in the city, kept me entertained outside of art class. She would often tell me about the latest drama from her dance class during one of our many late-night outings. As usual, we had decided to earn some overtime by waiting until the staff from the 4pm to midnight shift to leave before promptly leaving without clocking out, only to return at 4 a.m. to clock out and gain free hours on the payroll. We would usually order a few pints of Ben & Jerry's and a Cosi sandwich, courtesy of Kozmo.com, to stave off any post-alcohol hangovers we would likely endure. I'm sure our folly at the Internet start-up easily contributed to its demise.

It was in those wee hours that we would crawl around the Lower East Side, hanging out, smoking clove cigarettes, and snacking at the Pink Pony or getting our drink-on at La Linea. I always preferred La Linea because we knew the DJ, which guaranteed me entry without ID and free drinks. We would slip in behind our old coworkers and smile at the bouncer who waved us in with the mention of the DJ's name. It was one evening where Shing-I and I sat together in a booth sipping our cocktails beside the DJ as he spinned some classic Tribe Called Quest songs.

"This girl hit me in class," Shing-I huffed. It's like, the third time she's done it. I get so sick of these bitches." I laughed at the humor of it. "It's only in the African dance class. I never have this problem in Haitian class. I don't see why you go if it's always the same drama." I took a drag on a clove cigarette.

"No, I really do like it, it's just some of the women in there are so bitchy, and they never stay in their spot." I couldn't relate. It seemed simple to me. In my class, you watch the teacher do a move. You copied him. You stayed in place. What could be so complicated? "You should really come, my friend cajoled. I think you'll like it." I grudgingly agreed, and a week later I showed up with her to my first Haitian dance class.

I arrived with a baggy pair of sweats, a T-shirt, and no clue. I felt absolutely ridiculous grinding and wiggling my body. I looked like a snake having a seizure, my chaotic arms in the opposite direction of my feet. I stepped on my toes, slapped other dancers with my flailing hands, and danced in whatever row I happened to wind up, to the fury of the other, more experienced, dancers. I laughed hysterically at myself, so much so that Shing-I asked if I was laughing because of the dance, or because I was actually enjoying it. I lied and said I liked it, but I really thought it was complete foolishness.

My friend convinced me to take another, less demanding, version of the first class, and even though I felt like an idiot, I did feel invigorated afterward. But if I had any intention of getting better, I would have to be consistent with it. And I would have to stop smoking for good. I was a little saddened at the smoking part. I was never addicted to smoking, but I did enjoy chasing swigs of Red Stripe with an occasional sweet taste of a clove cigarette. Then again, looking at all those hot women in the class, with their tight abs and firm asses inspired me to want to stick with it. Little did I know that dance was to become the vehicle in which I traveled through time, space, emotions, and lovers.

Lovers like Abdoulaye.

ABDOULAYE

I never thought that I would become so involved in the world of African Diaspora dance. But there was just something about the beat of the drum that aroused a deep sexual awakening in me every time my bare feet touched the wood floor and caused my hips to gyrate with sensual abandon. As a child growing up in a predominantly white neighborhood, it never occurred to me that I could enjoy something I considered so primitive, so black. I was so far removed from the appreciation of my own origins that I often settled for mere platitudes of blackness. I had never envisioned myself as some Earth mother, head-wrapped, ankara-wearing type of girl, which was the extent of my understanding of other kinds of blackness. The closest I came to this was watching Erykah Badu on MTV. I lived on the upper west side, went to art school, read manga, fucked punk rockers, hung out at CBGB's, and scoured the Lower East Side for the bodegas that didn't card for beer. These leanings were not what I considered black, and so I struggled in the belief that I was stuck somewhere in the chasm of white identity in a black body.

But now, ironically at the suggestion of my Chinese co-worker, I was inside of an African dance studio in a skimpy tank top, leggings, and a sarong, writhing to the hypnotic beat of the hand-beaten drum. The walls pulsated with sex and sweat as feet and writhing bodies moved with the primal drumming made by hands slapping wooden drums wrapped in animal skin. The dance in and of itself was sex. It not only made me feel sexy, but I literally wanted sex after class. So it was no surprise that I played out my sexual fantasies with a collection of beautiful African drummers, dancers, and other musicians. And Abdoulaye.

When I first saw him, it was on a typical, busy spring evening in the studio. The ruckus of the first night class was already underway, though a steady stream of dancers were still arriving for class. I was waiting on line to pay for class and there he was. He was about six feet, not exceedingly handsome, but charismatic as hell. He had a smile brighter than the African sun on the sands of the Sahara that reflected off his dark-roasted chocolate skin. Abdoulaye had strolled into the place, chatting with a slew of musicians, and we briefly locked eyes. He turned back to his crew, said a few words in French, and then turned back to me.

"Do you happen to know if they have any mango Snapple?" His voice was light and smooth, yet confident. As the words rolled off his heart-shaped lips, I thought of all the places I would lick his body and turn him out.

"No, I haven't asked."

"Are you going to take my class?" he asked.

"Actually, I'm here for the Haitian class."

"Oh really? I thought Jean-Pierre was away for the summer?" he responded nonchalantly. I panicked. I hadn't anticipated going to another class. Not only did I suck at dancing, but I didn't want to look like a fool in a new class while I gawked at this man. Just then the young intern at the front desk announced that the Haitian class had been canceled. Great. I really didn't want to miss a workout, but I surely didn't want to make a fool of myself in a new class with a hot teacher. Luckily my friend Shing-I walked in.

"Hey, Haitian class is canceled," I told her. She slumped.

"Oh well, I guess we'll just take African." She saw the worried look on my face. "Don't worry, I'll help you with the steps. It'll be fun." I was somewhat relieved but uneasy at the thought of having to display my ineptitude at dancing to this hot teacher I had just met. Surely any attraction He had for me would dissipate as soon as I took two steps on the dance floor. At least with Shing-I near me, I could take this new class with someone familiar who would help me take the edge off. We paid for class and went inside the main studio where a student was doing the warm-up. I stayed in the corner by the door, while my best friend glided comfortably to the front of the room.

Suddenly Abdoulaye's booming voice took over the room as He danced in through the entrance, right by the corner I decided to hide myself in, taking over the warm-up and startling the student who had been leading the class.

"Hey! And 1, 2, 3, 4 . . ." he shouted in a singsong voice. He tapped the woman who had been doing the warm-up on her shoulder. "Thank you." She smiled sexily, glided back to her spot on the dance floor, her shoulders back and her nose up high. He jumped right in without missing a beat. I moved to the beat, trying to keep up, and focused on myself in the mirror, to keep from losing my step. For a second I looked up at him and saw him looking at me, and I stumbled slightly. He smiled.

Abdoulaye's body was lithe but toned, but sometimes he

would lift his shirt to wipe the sweat off his brow to expose his well-defined abdominal muscles. He wore his hair closely shaven so that he had the appearance of being bald in a certain light. I knew very little about him, except when I heard his name being brought up in conversations, though I could never put a face to the name. The basis of what I learned about him was from what I heard in whispers in the dressing room. A chauvinist. A thief. A snake. A ladies' man. A womanizer.

"He's a fucking pig," a sultry East African woman hissed as she stomped out of the dressing room one night. Yet all of the women in Abdoulaye's presence adored his beaming smile and corny jokes. He flirted with all of them, even though he had three kids (plus a rumored additional two, one in California and another overseas) and a wife. A white wife. It was of no consequence to the sisters there that tried to get a piece of him. They all had a chance and would shake their asses the hardest to see if he would notice, as he often did. The fact that his wife was white made the competition stiffer because all the white girls knew they had a chance—maybe an advantage—too. And if you were Asian, you tripled your chances. You were an automatic winner. This man was an equal opportunity player.

The warm-up wasn't so bad, but the actual dancing portion was a disaster. I couldn't make heads or tails of the moves. Unlike the Haitian class, where Jean-Pierre would do each move in a sequence, this teacher seemed to start the moves from the middle, and then add a slew of steps once the drummers came in.

I was completely lost and watched as my girlfriend and the rest of the class flawlessly seamed the different portions of the choreography together. I slid to the back of the room as the class jumped in rhythm, and when they all came together to form a circle and do individual solos, I slid out of the studio into the dressing room and got dressed.

After class, Abdoulaye made an announcement about a Senegalese Sabar show and party he was hosting up in Harlem. I had never taken Sabar, and he didn't teach this kind of dance, so I found it odd that he was throwing this kind of a party. He approached me with a flyer outside the classroom.

"You should come. I think you'll like it." I was hypnotized by his deep stare and averted my eyes to the flyer. "It's tonight."

"This looks exciting," I replied. "I'll see what I'm doing later on." I was already trying to figure out what I would wear.

~

As soon as I got home, I speed dialed all of my non-romantic male companions. I needed to show up with a man for several reasons: For one, the party started at midnight and I didn't want to travel alone from Brooklyn to Harlem by myself. Second, I didn't want to show up with another female who would detract attention away from me when I would inevitably bump into him. Third, I didn't want to seem overly available by showing up dateless. So I called my friend Kendu, who was a few years younger than I and lived in my building. He had nothing to do and figured he would hang out in the city and maybe pick up a few girls at a party in Harlem. For him, it was a win-win situation.

~

It was nearly 1 a.m. when we arrived and the show had just started to kick off. We handed over our tickets and walked into the auditorium. The entrance was lined two-deep with people spanning the perimeter of the room. I turned to Kendu to gauge his comfort level.

"What do you think?"

"It's cool. I see some fly-ass African chicks here. I'm about to get me a piece!" he joked, scanning the room. Just then, without notice Abdoulaye approached me in the darkness. He squeezed my arm lightly and when I turned he kissed me on the lips. He was so swift and smooth that I was taken aback, and as he let his hand fall down easily along my backside, I felt a jolt of electricity shoot down to my core. His brazenness both shocked and intrigued me, and his lips felt soft like fresh, sweet, Southern sponge cake.

"So you made it," he said, over the drums.

"Yeah, this is cool," I laughed nervously.

"Are you enjoying yourself?"

"Well, I just got here. I'm sure it will be good." The drums had gotten louder. Near the stage, a group of elaborately dressed women in brightly colored African dresses and head wraps began dancing the sabar, as the star singer of the evening came out to perform. He mentioned something in my ear, but I couldn't make anything out because of the drums, so I simply nodded. When I turned to look at him, he was gone, a ghost blended in the darkness.

"Damn, who was that dude? That nigga swooped in like gangbusters." Kendu was beside himself.

"Oh, just one of my dance teachers," I replied.

"Well damn, whatch'yall do in dance class?" he asked, clearly impressed by the man's debonair approach. "Shit, I need to go to dance class and get me some ass!" I laughed at Kendu's ability to take the edge off things and make me feel at ease. It reminded me of why I loved my male friends more than my female ones. The electricity of my encounter with the beautiful dancer still lingered, and it was all I could think of for the rest of the night. That man made me want to book a trip to Africa right then and there. By 4 a.m., the party was over, but I hadn't seen Him since Kendu and I first arrived, even though I searched the crowds in vain. He had me strung out and I hadn't even fucked him yet.

~

The next day I wrestled with the thought of taking his class. I didn't want to seem too desperate, but I hadn't felt this giddy for a man since I fell in love for the first time in New York City. I was itching for a new experience, and I had to have him. I was a little annoyed that he had just disappeared on me like that, without ever approaching me again, the night before. Maybe it was the same thing he did to countless other women. Still, I wasn't ashamed to experiment.

The one thing I dreaded was the actual class. I couldn't dance for shit, and I knew that. Plus, I wasn't the thinnest girl on the block, but I did know how to use my ample curves to my advantage. I got a pedicure, slipped on a tube top and leggings, and added a colorful sarong to my waist, since I didn't have any of the more traditional wraps that I saw the other women in class wearing. I arrived a little late so that I could slip into the routine unnoticed. As soon as I walked in the room, I got a booming salutation.

"Welcome to class! You're late!" I threw my bag and bottled water to the back of the room and shrunk into a spot on the dance floor, behind the more experienced dancers. "No, come over here." He made a gesture that directed me toward the center of the room in front of the mirror, next to one of his regular students. She sneered at me and adjusted herself in the mirror. I could have died. "You need to be able to see the steps." And look like a complete ass in front of the other dancers, I thought.

We did a series of calisthenics and jumps before I just about gave up. I was exhausted and wanted desperately to run to the back of the room to grab my water. Luckily, he stopped the music and allowed us to take a break so that he could count the students in the class. I was just about to walk out of the room to the bathroom when he caught me by the arm.

"Can you do a class count? I need to use the bathroom. Just write the number of students down on a piece of paper and leave it at the front of the room."

I nodded to him and began counting the students who were conversing in their own little cliques. A crowd of women shot me an angry glare. I ignored them and counted about twenty-four students before writing them down on a scrap of paper that he gave me. I thought of scribbling a little heart, a note, or something a little devious. I wanted him to remember me among this crowd of writhing, scantily-clad beauties. Remembering my limited French from college I scribbled:

Je veut mettre la chocolate fondu sur ton bite et se leche . . .

I wrote down my phone number, followed by a circled "24", the number of students in the class. Just as I finished writing my note, he reached down and grabbed the paper out of my hand, while I skipped back to my spot. He read the note, straight-faced, and motioned to the intern from the front desk to take down the number on the official sign-in sheet. As he began the routine, I looked at him for any signs of disapproval, careful to avoid locking eyes with him. He ignored me for the rest of the class. Great. I had a chance with the hottie and I blew it.

~

When I finally made it home, I showered and thought about the effects of what I had done during class. What if someone else had seen it? What if He told other people about what I had written? What if all the musicians caught wind and took it upon themselves to ask me for sexual favors? My head was flooded with questions. I didn't want to stop taking dance class, because I actually enjoyed learning when I wasn't making a fool of myself. But the thought of embarrassing myself every time I would see him in the studio made me shrink inside. I plopped down on the couch and stared at the ceiling wallowing in my thoughts. And then my cell phone rang.

"Hello?" I answered.

"Hi, it's me." I could recognize Abdoulaye's unmistakably charming voice through the phone.

"Oh, hi." I was completely caught off-guard.

"So what's going on?"

"I'm just relaxing, about to have dinner," I stuttered and then took a deep breath. "So I guess you got my note?" I started, trying to make small talk.

"What note are you talking about?" I laughed. He was so full of shit.

"The note I gave you in class."

"I don't recall. What did it say?" This man was pulling my leg. He wanted me to talk dirty to him. I took another deep breath, laughed nervously, and translated what I wrote.

"Is that so?" He laughed sexily. "And would that be with

dark chocolate or milk chocolate?"

"Oh dark chocolate, most definitely. They say it's very healthy." I was feeling a little more confident now.

"Hmmm. Well, have you ever done this before? I mean, I prefer that you have a little bit of experience. It's all fun and games until somebody gets hurt."

"I can assure you that I know what I'm doing. You won't be disappointed." He laughed again.

"All this talk about chocolate. What else do you enjoy doing?"

"I love to travel. I've mainly traveled to Europe, but since I've started taking class at the studio, I feel like I may want to go to Africa."

"Oh really? I would suggest Senegal. It's a beautiful country. French colonized. The food, culture—everything is beautiful."

"Sounds interesting. One of my girlfriends recommended Ghana as a first trip to Africa, since they speak English there."

"Eh, it's okay. Dakar is much better, trust me." We laughed a bit, and I felt a little more at ease. "So what else do you like?"

"I'm into art and music. I'm actually a visual artist. I play the flute occasionally, when I have a little spare time."

"How long have you been playing the flute?"

"For about ten years. My jaws are really toned." I cringed at my cheesy line.

"Is that so? Well, you'll have to perform for me for sometime." I laughed coquettishly.

"Whenever you'll have me. Listen, I've gotta run. I have a ton of assignments to do and I need to get up early for work tomorrow. Can I call you back?"

"No, I'll call you. Sweet Dreams."

"Good night." And I hung up.

~

In my junior year of college, my father had fallen ill with complications from diabetes. He stopped working, and was unable to support my student lifestyle. I was on my own, and I started working jobs to pay my own rent and bills and provide what little I could for my father. I had taken a few small jobs as a web or graphic designer after college, depending on the needs of any said company, but my heart just wasn't in it. I thought I took the safe route by picking a field that had guaranteed jobs, but I just wasn't having any fun. I recognized that the bills had to be paid, that I needed to get some goals for my life, and move up in the world, but I just wasn't ready to settle down into any sort of monotonous life. By the age of twenty-two I already had some work experience and had had the luxury of traveling throughout Europe extensively. But I still wasn't finished seeing what was out there. While scouring the job listings at my alma mater that summer, I came across a listing for a job as a fashion assistant at an up-and-coming urban fashion magazine. Granted, I had no experience actually assisting anyone in any fashion. The closest I got to that experience was creating a jpeg of clothes and accessories for some fashion website where I interned. But I figured I would give it a shot. I sent in my résumé and surprisingly got an interview within a few days.

I arrived at the publishing house, in the center of Times Square. It was November, and the first chill of winter had just begun to settle in. It was easy enough getting through security. The guard probably thought I was interviewing for a position in the mailroom. I wasn't dressed particularly fashionably. In fact, I was probably achingly boring. I wore a white button-down collared shirt, a strand of pearls, a slim pair of dark denim jeans, and a pair of gold-embroidered flats. I thought twice about wearing the jeans for an interview, but then again, I didn't take the interview seriously. I didn't give a shit because I was a graphic designer, after all, and thought I had a slim chance at getting this gig anyway. At best, I could always say that I set foot inside the offices of a fashion magazine.

As I sat in the foyer waiting to be called in by the editor for my interview, a lanky, imposing woman neared the glass doors. She had to be over six feet tall. Her hair was shaped into a boyish cut with a long and heavy bang colored a startling cerulean. She wore a fitted black skirt suit of which I guessed was Yves Saint Laurent, based on the previous night I had spent scanning fashion dictionaries online. Her look was accented with black tights, and a pair of five-inch stilettos outrageously adorned with peacock feathers. Her voice boomed with importance as she discussed her upcoming social calendar. Immediately the air in the office shifted as backs sat straight in chairs, shoes changed from crusty sneakers to painfully high stilettos, and assistants scurried in the closets, preparing their looks for the next editorial review. She was followed by her flamboyant male assistant who had to be in his late thirties, and whom I assumed to be gay. He was wearing a sharp brown three-piece suit and carrying her coat and a few pillows as they walked toward her corner office. She turned to look at me and gave me a head-to-toe look over. I've never felt so lowly. I thought I noticed a faint smirk. Maybe it was disappointment that there was someone who came to the offices of a fashion magazine looking so . . . blah.

My mind drifted to thoughts of Abdoulaye. Since that first call, he hadn't spoken to me, and I wondered why. Maybe I had come on too strong for him, and he wanted a little more mystére. Maybe I wasn't hot enough. In the weeks following our encounter, I took his class sparingly, while trying out other classes during the same time slot, so that I could get a glimpse of him without having to endure an entire two hours of dancing, sweating, and salivating over the man. The way he consumed me was entrancing, exhilarating, and almost mythic. He was my God.

I replayed that night in Harlem over and over again: the smell of his cologne, the brush of his hand along my body, how the way his lips pressed against mine in the dark. His omnipresent being flooded my thoughts and took me to an addictive high that ruined my concentration on a daily basis.

He made me fascinated with the idea of Africa. When

I thought of him, I thought of what Africa would be like, hot, sensual and exotic. I desperately wanted to go. I began making arrangements to go to Dakar, Senegal, on my own, with a few associates I had met in my Brooklyn neighborhood. The money came, amazingly, by me doing an absurd amount of odd jobs and freelance work, so that I had just enough money to purchase a round-trip ticket. It was a bold move, going to another country with a family I barely knew, but I figured a solo trip there—as opposed to a typical dance group tour with a teacher-- might give me a leg up on all the other females in class who vied for his attention. A steady, sharp click of stilettos quickly brought me back to reality.

This time it was the interviewing editor who came out and did the same once over on me that the editor-in-chief had done. Only this editor was not as put together, though she was dressed head to toe in designer clothing. She just seemed a bit frazzled to me, the type to always be behind deadline, always late to an appointment. Her weave was ratty, like a poor attempt at the bed-head look, and she barely had any makeup on. But her shoe and bag game was on point. I knew she could name any accessory you happened to be wearing, as her desk was flanked with heels with the names Jimmy Choo, Sergio Rossi, and YSL embossed on their inner soles. Marc Jacobs bags, stacks of hat boxes from a PR firm I didn't recognize, and several brown paper bags with countless goodies surrounded her desk.

"Hi, I'm Natasha. I am the senior accessories editor for

bags, shoes, and swimwear. So. Tell me why you want to work here." Her voice was a carefully crafted hybrid of Valley Girl and Gossip Girl. By looking at her I could tell she was African—maybe Nigerian—but it was obvious that she wanted to reflect anything but. I remember reading in a *Women's Wear Daily* that she was from Texas. Apparently, her boss, the fashion director, was the same boss at their former publication and brought her along when their division was sacked.

"Well, I was always interested in fashion. As a web design-er, I have done a lot of work for several online commercial fashion companies, and I just wanted to see what it would be like working from the editorial side." Smart answer, I thought. She wrote a note on a piece of company letterhead and handed it to me.
"Can you pronounce this designer?" I looked down at the words and thought for a brief moment. I knew I saw this designer's name before.

CESARE PACIOTTI

I wanted to say "Say-ZAR-Pah Chee-AH-Tee," but I didn't think that was right.

"Cheh-Zah-RAY Patch-YAH-tee." I even added a little flourish to the R for extra effect.

"Wow, you're the first person I've interviewed who got that right. When are you available to start?" I couldn't believe my ears. Was this lady shitting me?

"Um, tomorrow, I guess."

"Great, be here tomorrow at 9 a.m. Actually, you'll be reporting to the jewelry editor. But come to see me first. And don't be late. Or I will fire your ass stat."

~

After a few weeks of dancing on a regular basis, I had gotten quite comfortable with moving in front of an audience. The more I practiced, the better I got, and the newer students began coming to me for help with the steps. I was starting to really feel myself, even though I knew I wasn't shit compared to the serious dancers in the more advanced classes.

I loved to dance, but hated going to class. Every day I had to fight the front-row bitches for a spot in front of the mirror. And then I had to side-eye said bitches whenever one of them felt special and couldn't bother to stay in their space. The politics of dance class were so foolish, yet the rules were a requisite for order on the dance floor. But once I got into the dance, I was in another realm. We would warm up with a playful Soukous and progress into the dance routine, which was usually a popular Guinea dance, but sometimes Abdoulaye mixed in some Senegalese Sabar, which was his favorite, for fun. Today, he was teaching Yankadi, a sensual flirtation dance that allowed our arms and hips to stroke the rhythm. The movement was like sex in artistic motion.

It was fall when I approached him after class to tell him

about my upcoming trip. The gaggle of flirting students had long gone, and there were only a few lingering women cleaning their bare feet from the dirt of the dance floor and stretching in the back of the room.

"So, I've decided to go to Dakar in December."

"Oh really?" His tone was indifferent. It was like we had never had a flirtatious conversation several weeks before. Apparently the smiles and jokes in class were just a marketing ploy for new and prospective students. He seemed to have had no recollection of our previous chat. "Who are you going with?"

"Well, I'm not going on a workshop trip; I'm just visiting the family of some friends." He didn't respond. In fact, he made no effort toward having a conversation, and seemed distracted as He gathered his belongings to leave the classroom. "I'll be there for about three weeks. Is there any place you could recommend?" "You should probably visit the major fabric market. It's called HLM. Hey, I gotta run. You have my e-mail? Shoot me an e-mail and I'll send you some suggestions."

And with that he was gone. I pondered the idea of meeting him in Africa, by some unlikely twist of fate. We would arrange a rendezvous in a busy open-air market, and then sneak off to have passionate sex in a stone-walled compound on a hot afternoon, the sun pouring into our room, onto our bed as we fucked furiously, his 90% dark cacao skin pounding my milk-chocolate flesh. But it was a dream, a fantasy.

~

As soon as I got home, I showered, ate, and sat down in front of my computer. What would I say? I didn't want to sound too eager, but to be at least charming, and somewhat sexy.

From: sxybareftdncer@yahoo.com
To: drumdancelife@yahoo.com

Hey,

I felt so hot in your class today. No, really. There were so many students that I nearly suffocated from the heat! Please get more fans! Anyway, I just wanted to remind you to give me that list of things to do while I'm in Dakar. Even though I'm not leaving until December, I wanted to get a head start on my planning.

Peace, Xoxo

How corny. I deleted and rephrased, added, then subtracted words, but ended up back where I started. I paused for a moment to see if there was anything sexy I could add. Whatever I wrote would have to double the impact of my first explosive statement on that fateful piece of paper several weeks before. I thought a while, but to my better judgment, I decided against it and just pressed SEND.

~

I walked in to the office at 9 a.m. on the dot, and the editor wasn't there. Actually, there was nobody there except for the art department. The graphic artists there were astonishingly unfashionable and unfazed. It was a wonder that they got hired at a slick and stylish urban fashion magazine. I should have known that the art departments were pretty much the same in any setting: comfortable work clothes geared at long days and nights sitting in front of a Mac clicking away at Photoshop. I took the time to poke around a bit. A plucky assistant was assorting and distributing the mail, while another one was busy dropping lattes off at the desks of some editors who would appear at any minute with their unreasonable demands. Then Natasha walked in. She had the air of a senior editor, but the rough edges of an intern. She walked to her desk and threw her pilled and tattered Valentino coat over the chair. She glanced over at me.

"Hey. So. You're going to be working in the closet today. We have a shitload of returns. I just got back from doing a shoot in Morocco, and we were delayed a few days. Vogue is on our ass for these sandals. Actually, take them and send them over there now. Call a messenger service. Make sure they are checked out of the system first." She then promptly shifted her attention from me to her computer screen. I didn't have a damn clue what it was she wanted me to do. All that I could process was Morocco. A shoot in Morocco. I imagined being in Marrakech, walking along the cluttered stalls filled with wildly colored trinkets, rugs, and glittering jewels. Was fashion going to be my ticket to unlimited trips around the world on someone else's dime? I salivated at the thought of flying to some far off destination every few weeks—for work, of course—exploring indigenous peoples and tasting exotic foods. I would do anything to get on a plane.

As I walked away from Natasha's desk, I bumped into a no-nonsense twenty-something woman who informed me that her name was Shireen, that she was the senior fashion assistant, and that if I wanted to survive here, I would take note of everything she told me. She handed me a notebook and a pen.

"You'll need this. Now come with me."

She led me around the corner, past the makeshift kitchen (people in fashion don't eat anyway, I figured), to the closet, which was adjacent to the copy machine and the water cooler. She turned the key and unlocked the door to what could only be described as a big girl's play land. Piles of shoes of every height and color cluttered the room, and racks of clothes sagged from the weight of black garment bags. On the back shelves were rows and rows of jewelry—necklaces, earrings, bracelets, and rings, in varying degrees of shimmer. Here and there, between nondescript garment bags, a glittering gown or piece of tulle poked out. The room was scattered with brown paper bags stapled shut, like oversized carry-out containers of inedible, delectable fashion. It was a beautiful mess.

"Your task is to get this room in order." I hung my head incredulously. I couldn't imagine getting through all of those mounds of clothes and shoes in my lifetime. But at least the organizing would give me time to quietly meditate on my possible future in fashion. I removed my shoes and blazer and got to work. I began by dumping random articles of clothing, heels, and accessories into common piles by category, carefully placing them so as not to scuff the items or rip any fine fabric. After about three hours I had begun to make headway. Then a flood of packages and garment bags came in from various PR agencies. Shireen ran in the room, frantic.

"Okay, all of these need to be unpacked and arranged for a run-through in the next hour. As you unpack these items, they need to be checked in and photographed." She handed me a Polaroid camera. "If you lose anything, it's your ass."

This little blip in my grand reorganizing of the fashion closet put a damper on my day. At this rate, I would never finish. I pushed aside a pile of clothing and bags with my foot and plopped myself down in the middle to start removing clothes from the bags. Opening each black nondescript garment bag was like experiencing Christmas over and over again, only you didn't get to keep the presents. Their contents were glittering ball gowns, slinky rhinestone-studded mini dresses, and sequin-encrusted bustiers. I wondered who would be wearing these over-the-top fashions, and, as if reading my mind, I overheard an editor talking about an upcoming shoot for "Mariah" in the kitchen corridor. I was giddy with excitement. Mariah? As in Carey? I wondered if I would meet her. I knew she was extravagant. Maybe we would have the shoot somewhere luxurious, like the South of France. From what I saw in the magazine's last issue, they had done a swimsuit issue that was shot in Tahiti, so I didn't think it was that much of a stretch. Whether they would take me—well, that was another rather unlikely possibility. As my mind drifted to the luxury yachts along the warm southern French coast, the editor-in-chief's assistant came in, this time in a beige checkered three-piece suit and shiny leather oxfords.

"Are we all set for the run-through?" he asked, glancing around the room. It had hardly been twenty minutes since Shireen had warned me about the upcoming review.

"It's almost ready," I lied, looking down at the half-opened pile of bags in the room.

"Okay, well we need to be ready ASAP. The Madame will be in to take a look in about ten minutes."

I scurried to get all the looks together, mentally noting the unpacked items as he sifted through the unopened garment bags on the rack. I tore through the brown bags on the floor filled with shoeboxes and lined all the shoes up in neat rows, while unzipping all the garment bags, simultaneously categorizing them by style, length, and color. It was an amazing feat. Within five minutes she came in; she was followed by the fashion director and Natasha.

"So what do we have?" she asked as she scanned the available items. She looked over the dresses and pulled out a shimmery turquoise mermaid silhouette gown. "This looks a little small, no?" She looked at me for an explanation.

"Mariah's stylist requested a size six," Shireen chimed in. The editor's assistant did a deadpan.

"A six?" he laughed, incredulously. "That bitch hasn't been a size six since the Heartbreaker album." I did my best to stifle a laugh and turned away to unpack a new series of bags that had just arrived. I opened the bags and placed the costume jewelry that was inside them on to black velvet display cases for the editors to review.

"And the shoes? What do we have?" She looked at the collection on the floor disdainfully. "Is this all we could get?" Her voice was strained.

"Well, everyone's getting ready for the MTV Music Awards, and Elle and Vogue are shooting their winter issues, but they said we could pick up our requests later on today," Natasha contributed eagerly. I looked on. This lady never had her shit together, I could tell. I wonder how she would keep her job.

"This selection isn't sufficient," the top editor snorted. "I need more options." Madame Editor picked up a pair of Pierre Hardy pumps. "No." She tossed them to the side, and picked up another. "No. No." Shoes were flying everywhere. Out of the fifty or so pairs, she chose two. "I need more Louboutins. Where are those new YSL Tribute pumps?"

"I'll call in and request them again," Shireen offered. I was overwhelmed. As I looked at the aftermath of the edit, I began to wonder if this was really how I was going to get to travel around the world. The fashions did make me feel giddy, but the drudgery that I was witnessing made fashion seem so ugly and slavish. Still, I pressed on, sorting, collecting, and organizing, and by 8 p.m., I finally packed away the last five-inch strappy Giuseppe Zanotti into a travel case bound for a Miami photo shoot that I would not be attending. A girl could dream.

~

A week into my new job I had plans to attend the opening gala for Alvin Ailey's new season. I absolutely could not miss it come hell or high water and I bought cheap nosebleed seats for the chance to be in attendance. Since starting this job, I had no time to dance; the hours were brutal, and by the time I finished for the day, I would barely have half an hour to dance, even if I took the latest evening class. When the weekends rolled around, I was starving to move, and indulged in triple class orgies on both days. I especially missed getting to see him as often, as he was part of the drive in my consistency with dancing. I did love the rush of the job, but the Ailey opening? I was not missing it. The performance of *Revelations* was what initially piqued my interest in dance in the first place.

When I was a freshman in college, I had worked for a wealthy, well-connected New York socialite, who was a respected patron of the arts. She was the kind of person who you always saw in the back of the playbill under Director's Circle, or some high status club of donors with serious money. I had graciously accepted an invitation to the spring gala opening of which Erykah Badu was the honorary chairwoman. I was elated for this fact alone, as she was one of my favorite artists at the time. I remember sitting in the first row, mesmerized as the principle dancers, draped in flowing white attire, commanded the stage. Their bodies were so beautiful, and strong, and black. I had never felt so moved. From then on, I vowed to dance, but ironically, it wasn't until Shing-I finally convinced me to step onto the dance floor that my vow became reality.

I quietly finished all of my clothing returns, skipping lunch, and working furiously so that when I left at 7 p.m., the closet was virtually spotless. I put on my coat, carrying a few brown bags for returns to be left in the main foyer, to use as my cover. Luckily, Shireen was not sitting at her desk, guarding all who entered, so I dropped the bags at reception for the delivery service and slipped out the door. I walked quickly to the train station, ducking the tourists who seemed to stop mid-step in Times Square. I hated Times Square with a passion. All the god-awful lights and all the slow people clogging the streets with no purpose at all, making it hard for all those with a real purpose to accomplish anything. I finally made it into the subway, where I caught the train uptown to 59th St Columbus Circle, where the new Ailey Center awaited.

~

The lights went down, the curtain opened, and a lone soaring, strong, black body appeared on the stage, commanding our attention and respect. Then more bodies appeared, moving to the beat of urban syncopation. They were draped in bold colors of fiery orange, yellow, fuchsia, lime green. They professed Love in seamless movement and rhythm, and I felt love. I felt passion and abandonment, anger, lies, and truths forsaken. There was a force on that stage that I'm not quite so sure the other audience members felt. I wanted to be there, and from my balcony seat, I almost leapt way down there to the stage, leaping without looking.

~

I returned to work the next day, and snuck into the closet, as if I didn't miss a thing. There was an upcoming shoot featuring a new actress named Zoe Saldana, and I needed to prepare the incoming looks for the edit happening that morning. As the first bags of clothing and shoes arrived, Shireen came in to tell me the good news.

"You're going on your first location shoot. I need you to be on your best behavior. Pay attention. Don't ask a lot of questions. Don't get in the way. And please don't fuck up." She also notified of me of the new fashion intern, Brianna, who seemed to know everybody, and acted as if she was an actual employee. She would be working with me in the closet. I figured it could only help me to have an extra set of hands in the closet, so I immediately showed her the check-in and check-out process, how to return a dress, how to call a messenger, how to make a fax. All the boring stuff.

Something about her annoyed me, though she never actually did anything wrong. I watched as, day after day, she would come in and immediately buy Starbucks hot chocolate for all the editors, on her dime. If there was one thing I hated, it was a kiss-ass. She had her cute little spunky curls and her Louis Vuitton pochette and Marc Jacobs heels. She always knew the trendy thing to do or say, at just the right time, and held the hearts of every editor in her pocket. I had my sensible flats, button-down flannel, and boy jeans. I minded my business and worked like a horse. I got shit done while she schmoozed. It irritated me, but I carried on. I had a shoot to prepare for the following morning and I would likely be in the closet all night while everyone else went out for drinks or to fabulous parties I was not invited to.

~

The next day I arrived at work earlier than the 8 a.m. call time so that I could peacefully scarf down a quick breakfast of croissant and coffee. It would be a long day and I couldn't afford to be fainting on set from an empty stomach. Too many key players in the industry would be there and I had hoped to capture a few prominent business cards for my next big career move.

The shoot was to take place at a mansion on Long Island, so we would need to set out at the stroke of 8 to try and beat traffic. Within ten minutes of my arrival several editors who were coming to the shoot arrived to check that all of the key pieces were ready and to square off any last minute details. Minutes later a flurry of interns and Brianna, the suck-up fashion assistant, appeared. Today she had bought rich, hot dark chocolate Starbucks Chantico for all of the editors. She was wearing another cute pair of Marc by Marc Jacobs pumps. I stared at her shoes and compared them to my scruffy Converse, built for running across set at a moment's notice. I was there to get shit done, and this princess was standing there working her own PR. Shireen came in.

"Okay, the trucks are downstairs. Let's start loading these garment boxes downstairs. Immediately the interns scrambled to grab garment bags, boxes, and any other items designated for the shoot. By the time I went to grab something, all of the items had been taken. I grabbed a clipboard and a check-in sheet so that I wouldn't be empty-handed, and piled into the SUV that would be taking us to the undisclosed location.

It was hard to focus on anything with all of the chattering interns in the vehicle. There were endless ramblings about everything and nothing at all. The magazine's editors were lucky enough to get their own town cars, so there was no need for them to share a ride with the lowly staff. I listened to music and daydreamed about dance and my future romance with the African dancer. Soon enough, we arrived at the location. It was a sprawling, slightly derelict estate, with wildflowers growing in every direction, and a dirt road that led to its entrance. The worn down exterior gave it a charming appearance, as it had come straight out of a Dickens novel. I took a deep breath of the late spring air. No sooner had we stepped out of the vehicle to stretch our feet than Shireen started barking orders.

"Everybody will be here in an hour so I want everything set up! You!" She pointed to a scrawny white boy in a cardigan, bow tie, and Converse. "Take those boxes to the second floor. Security will direct you." She pointed to me and I walked over to her. "Follow him and make sure he doesn't lose anything." I was surprised at Shireen's confidence in me. She continued yelling directions until we were all inside the empty mansion.

I immediately began unpacking shoes and dresses and arranging them by style, color, and shape so that the stylists and editors would have an easier time selecting their pieces for the shoot. I still had no idea who the actual star of this shoot would be, but I was sure it would be someone fabulous. I had selected a room that was a little far off from the main staircase and foyer where the photographer and set designer had begun setting up for the main shots. While I worked alone, a security guard entered with the jewelry editor. Apparently he would be watching over the ten million dollars' worth of diamonds that the star would be wearing for this pictorial. Harry Winston had sent over its own security detail. The thought of being around all those jewels made me nervous, so I went to another room, where a seamstress was adjusting several custom corsets for the star.

"Those are stunning!" I commented of a rhinestone-studded purple version.

"Yes, they are," she replied in a deep Russian accent, "but they will never fit her. They are way too small. Whoever told us Tyra Banks was a size four was delusional." I sighed. How tragic it was to see yet another celebrity in complete denial of reality.

~

Tyra arrived about an hour later with a huge entourage. By then all the assistants and interns had settled in comfortably by the craft services table in the mansion's kitchen. I had just added some lox to my cream cheese bagel when Shireen called me in to one of the parlor rooms on the floor that had been converted into the official dressing room. I walked in, and I was there with Shireen, Tyra's stylist, and the star herself, who stood, bare breasted in a pair of g-string panties. I expected her to be a complete diva, like the person I saw everywhere in the media, but instead, she simply looked up at me insecurely.

"Can you go over to the seamstress and get the corsets? We want to start with the ball gown looks first," Shireen ordered. I literally ran to the seamstress and collected all of the pieces, even though some of them weren't finished. As I ran back to the dressing room, I could feel the buzz of my cell phone. I reached in my pocket to see that it was Abdoulaye. Please not now, I thought, and pressed IGNORE. The phone buzzed again, and I let it go. I was not about to be distracted by this man, no matter how infatuated I was with him. My career was just too important. I handed off the corsets and went back to the kitchen to enjoy some breakfast.

The shoot was well underway and Tyra was in all her princess glory as she stood with her gown draped over a fabulously decayed staircase. Her neck gleamed with diamonds and huge fans gave the illusion of her blowing curls, which were adorned by a sparkling rhinestone tiara. I stood behind the editor-in-chief and her assistant, watching in awe. But when Tyra turned around I saw a horrific concoction of tape, pins, and spandex, holding the poor corset together. The assistant leaned in to his boss, confidently.

"Too bad none of the pieces fit. We'll have to shoot all of the looks from the front." The editor shook her head in disdain.

~

Shireen had sent me home early in a town car to hand deliver a dress to the offices of Yves Saint Laurent because the piece was needed for a high-profile shoot in Vogue. I was relieved to leave and not have to pack up the clothing and accessories from the shoot, which were likely in a cluttered mess all over the mansion. In the car I had a chance to nap and check over my messages. The first message was from Abdoulaye.

"Hey, where are you? Are you coming to class tonight? Call me." I already knew I wouldn't make it to class, but I would not pass up the opportunity to meet with him. He was so close, I could taste him.

~

A few weeks had passed, and I had grown to love my job. The editors in the beauty department were especially nice and they allowed me to rummage through the beauty closet for an endless supply of full-sized product samples. I was in heaven. Natasha had set me up with the task of RSVPing for all the upcoming fashion shows in Paris on her behalf. She had a select number of shows that were musts, and others that she didn't really care about. She left those in a bin that she labeled "Trash". While I was calling up all of the agencies, I decided that it wouldn't hurt if I took down a few numbers and e-mail addresses. I figured I could do some assistant styling work on the side. I was finally feeling confident in what I was doing, being able to spout designer names and labels at the snap of a finger or the glance of a sequin. Brianna stopped by the desk.

"What are you doing?" she asked innocently enough.

"Oh, I'm just RSVPing to some shows for Natasha, and taking some notes."

"Oh, okay!" she chirped. And then she sauntered off to kiss some editor's ass.

I went back to work and began sorting through the trash pile. I knew that Natasha couldn't attend those events because her schedule was full. I snatched the invites off her desk, slid them in my back pocket, and went outside for a coffee break. Outside I went to the Internet café on 42nd St, and RSVPed to all the shows from the invites that I had stuffed in my pocket. The ones without e-mail addresses I called up directly, and stored the information in my phone. All was well in the war of fashion.

~

A week had passed since my invitation heist and I happily skipped around the office, eagerly anticipating the shows, the parties, and perks that came with them. Shireen called me to her desk. "What were you doing?" Apparently little Miss Bri wasn't so innocent after all. She saw me sneaking the invites when I thought no one was looking.

"I was getting rid of some things that were going in the trash."

"But you took some of those things. And none of it was yours. What made you think you could take them?"

"It was trash. I really didn't think I was doing anything wrong."

"Okay, you know what, you don't need to come back tomorrow. You're fired."

I pleaded with her, but she wouldn't budge. So I did what I do best whenever I wanted something. I cried. A look of panic came across Shireen's face.

"Stop it! Stop crying." I sobbed a little louder. If too many people heard me, it would cause a scene, and she would look bad, like she couldn't handle a situation. "Okay, okay! Look. You fucked up. I'm going to give you another chance. I am watching you." She took a deep breath and looked at me sternly. "Don't be late. Don't steal shit. Do what you're told. Do it before you're told. That is it. Now go."

Later that night I received a message from Shireen. I listened with dread. I was sure that she had changed her mind, and I sat on my bed to take in the news.

"Listen, you don't have to come in tomorrow." My heart sank. "The magazine is closing. There's no more funding. We all have to be cleared out by Friday. You can come in if you want, to finish out the week. You can even pick up your pay. They'll cut you a check down in payroll."

As I listened, a sudden wave of sadness came over me. This new passion that I loved had just flat-lined and I felt aimless and empty inside. A place where I had given so much of my passion, in so little time was now nearly gone. Tears welled up in my eyes and landed on a colorful thick cardstock invitation that sat among many others. Through my blurred vision I could make out some of its words:

JILL SANDER
AUT MN – WI ER
02 FEV R
RUE GOE L S
PARIS
RS P:
rsvp@ k dny.c m

PARIS

Even with the collapse of The Fashion Magazine, I knew that I enjoyed being in the world of magazine publications. Without realizing it, I had developed a sudden, uncontrollable desire to be in the frenzy of fashion media. The superficial world of glamorous photo shoots, parties, and celebrity appealed to me now, and I developed an insatiable appetite for the nightlife. I was lucky enough to establish a friendly relationship with the girls at the public relations houses, for clothes and invites, despite the run-in with the conniving intern at The Fashion Magazine. I couldn't be mad at her. She was just playing the game. I worked the field by exchanging products that the magazine received freely, in exchange for fashion favors, like clothes and shoes to wear to a club with a tight door, or an industry party. She was just playing the game, too.

It was 2005 and magazines were still hot at the time. I landed a job as a freelancer at The Magazine Company just before circulations began to decline, when editors still spent lavishly on car services, clothes, and expense accounts. I was ushered into the doors of this magazine conglomerate, with its fancy new building, designer café, and private sushi chef. I couldn't wait to get my hands inside a beauty closet, or drape my hands across a silk Marchesa gown. I would take a mile if they gave me an inch.

Somehow, I managed to find a job where I could be paid to work on my own terms with little or no objection from my superiors. I loved my job because it didn't require much work at all. It wasn't permanent—more or less a fulltime freelance gig that allowed me to come and go as I pleased. I basically got paid to read, research and archive magazines and pictures all day. I could sit and read a magazine, get a fashion or beauty tip, blog about it, read gossip websites, and stay up to date on the latest trends. Some days when I finished my work early, I would sneak out and go on look-sees at fashion studios to preview the upcoming collections. Nobody noticed because I always managed to get my work done on time with stellar results.

My cubicle was perfect. Walled on all sides, I felt as if I truly had my own office, where I could make phone calls, arrange meetings, and be an entrepreneur in my free time. My boss, Mr. X, worked on the other side of the floor, in a glass office, so I remained completely undisturbed, except for when he needed to grab a cup of coffee. Fortunately, the kitchen was on my side of the office, so I could conveniently sneak in for a snack, and only occasionally bump into my boss, or any other important person.

My desk was my personal hub. Day after day, I would receive product samples, various items to try or books to read, and sometimes clothing. Then I would leave and go to a fashion show, or a look-see. Since Bryant Park was a hop and a skip away, it was easy to get away with it. I felt a rush as I walked up those steps into the fashion tent, past security, with my invitations in hand. And soon I would be in Paris, with these same beautiful people, in a beautiful city, doing beautiful things. But above it all, my passion to fly never escaped me.

My grandmother infected me with the travel bug, although

I didn't realize this until many years later as I reflected on my many years of traveling. I went on plenty of trips with my mom—London, Paris—but I now know that something was embedded in me in that '85 Riviera. When I entered adulthood and semi-independent living I found the freedom to go anywhere and see anything. No kids, no mortgage. No miserable marriage, no midlife crisis. I certainly didn't think I was searching for myself. I knew where I was—in my ripe twenties without a care in the world, with a zest for life, and a determination to live it fully. I started young on this journey and I just knew that it was the seeds that were sown when I was a child that ignited this fire inside me to see and explore the world. My travel obsession went into full throttle during my long stint at The Magazine Company. With my new, higher income, I finally had the money to fund my habit.

~

New York Fashion Week was nearly over, and I still hadn't booked my ticket to Paris. It was a crazy thing to do, to book a trip when I had just landed a new job, and had another trip planned a few months down the line, but I told myself that it was a job-related experience. Since I was a freelancer anyway, they really couldn't say much. The worst scenario would be that I would get fired, but when I told my boss of my plans, he was surprisingly ok with them, since it was fashion-related. Luckily for me, part of Paris Fashion Week fell on a holiday, so I booked a trip that would include the holiday and the weekend so there would be minimal impact of my non-presence at work.

I pored over all my invites where I had scribbled seat assignments. It had been almost too easy securing a spot at some of the most coveted Paris fashion shows, and after I had made my first call to an RSVP line, I gathered enough confidence to call as many as I could—even ones where I had no invite. It never hurt to try. By my fifth call, I was talking like an old pro, name-dropping and listing my credentials when I received callbacks from suspicious public relations managers. I was officially in.

With my newfound obsession with fashion, I found I was spending less and less time at the dance studio. I knew I had to dance to keep up my appearance, but the inevitable draw of the fashion world drew me down an inescapable path of a new, more glamorous world. I chose fashion shows and late night parties over drum circles and flirtatious conversations with the charismatic man who stole my heart only a few months before.

I sat in my little office cubicle, researching the cheapest flights online. The best I could do was Air India, a random airline that got me a dirt-cheap ticket out of Newark airport to Paris. With no place to stay once I got to France, I whipped out my credit card, entered the details, and proceeded with the purchase.

~

I was brimming with energy from the experience of my

first fashion week in New York, and I had to keep up the momentum. With a few stashed Paris runway invites, some borrowed Louboutins, and a bit of extra cash from overtime, I managed to find my way to Paris. My friend Gwenyth had put me in contact with Tristan, an old childhood friend from France. The fates aligned, Tristan and I connected, and I had free accommodations for the week. It was perfect.

I boarded the last flight out of Newark and ten hours later was standing in Charles de Gaulle airport with an old Louis Vuitton duffle bag. Even though I was exhausted, I decided to make a pit stop at the Eiffel Tower to take some fashion photos of myself for posterity. I hopped on the Métro and was there in no time. I dipped into a restroom right under the tower and slipped on a pair of my impossibly high, black-studded Louboutin booties. As I walked out of the restroom, the attendant just stared at my feet in awe. "Impossible!" she gasped as I treaded lightly on the pavement. I made my way to a nearby bench and snapped some photos.

By the time I finished, I was tired and hungry. I decided to take my chances and go to Tristan's, even though I hadn't called and could not for the life of me find a pay phone. I made my way to a quaint little alley off Rue St. Antoine in the Bastille section. I found the large wooden doorway and followed the directions to open the coded door. With relief, the door clicked and I opened it to a dark foyer with a narrow spiral staircase before me. I searched in vain for a light switch, but found none. So I walked up the stairs in complete darkness, until I reached the second floor, which, when counted with the ground level was, in fact, the second. I scrambled in the dark, near the foot of the door searching for the key to the apartment that Tristan had promised would be there. The key wasn't there. All the commotion must have startled the lone neighbor on his floor because she opened the door ajar and stared at me as I shuffled around.

"Tristan?"

"No, a friend of Tristan's. I'm just visiting." The old woman stepped out of the doorway, pressed on a button that provided a light for a winding staircase, and then slipped back into her apartment. I continued to search for the spare key. I looked everywhere—under the staircase, in the crevices, down the stairs. Maybe it had fallen in a crack as the hall light flickered on and off? A few more hopeless minutes passed before the automatic light went out completely. I sat down on the stairs, defeated. The woman reappeared at her door and shuffled in the darkness to find the hidden switch for the hallway light. With a click, the light returned, and I got a good look at the stocky, white-haired woman.

"I can't find the key," I told her. She gestured me inside her apartment. I could tell that she spoke no English, and I didn't waste time trying to convey my concerns in anything but French. "Tristan usually comes home around 8 p.m. I can always hear his bike." She took a peek outside the window into the alley below at the roar of a moped. It was someone else. "Would you like something to drink?"

I nodded as she made her way to her makeshift kitchenette. Her apartment was painted a muted yellow and pictures of all sizes, in various gilded frames, decorated the walls. I sat down on the tawny sofa and gazed at the small tchotchkes that cluttered her living room shelves. A dingy, run-down television was broadcasting the news. Here in this tiny apartment in Paris, I was reminded that grandmothers around the world were probably all the same.

She offered me some tea and sat down. "Tristan is just like my son. He's young, an artist, and comes in and out." She showed me a picture. "I miss my real son. Sometimes he visits me and we go on trips to the south, or have lunch on Sunday. How do you know Tristan?"

"We were introduced through a mutual friend," I responded in broken French. I thought of Gwenyth at that moment. I had bumped into her in a dance class quite literally, as she was in a drum-induced trance. She was a bit of a hippy with a fascination for probiotics and P. Diddy. Her mismatched values created a contentious, yet exciting friendship between us. That, and her ever-present flakiness. Tall and healthy, with soft olive skin, and the jet-black silken hair of a Chinese virgin, she raised hell on the streets of Soho with her slinky, semi-sheer, bohemian skirts and her little black book full of yogis, tantric instructors, rap stars, and Wall Street hedge fund managers. She always seemed to be glowing, from a yoga class, a homemade tincture, or a stop at a mosque for spiritual rejuvenation. I never met someone who so effortlessly segued between a vegan raw food diet and a fur-filled fashion show at Bryant Park. We would spend nights together in New York City, randomly dipping into African dance class at The Studio, to a raw food restaurant, and then up to an über-chic, ultra-exclusive section of a club whose owner she knew, of course. She was one of those friends whom I cherished for the new experiences, but loathed for the very randomness that made her attractive to me.

The old woman jumped up at the sound of another moped in the alleyway. It had to be him. She listened quietly for the latch of the main door to open. A few shuffles came from below, and we could hear the steady footsteps climbing the narrow winding staircase. The steps finally landed on our floor and we heard the light switch. The woman stuck her head outside her door. It was Tristan. I poked my head out from behind hers, and Tristan and I locked eyes. I had a moment. Was I about to fall into a clichéd infatuation with a French man I had just met? No, not me, the smart city girl. I knew better.

He stood about six feet tall with pale skin, lush pink lips, a fresh buzz cut, and a five o'clock shadow. He wore a wicked grin on his face. "So, you've come. I didn't think you had made it because I didn't hear from you today." True. I never called him because I wasn't fortunate to have a global-use cell phone, nor could I figure out how to use the coinless pay phones I found on the street. I was completely left to fate. "That is why I took the key. I thought you weren't coming."

The old French woman smiled and waved us good-bye and I stepped onto the short landing into Tristan's small apartment. "Are you hungry?" he asked. I was starving and broke, but didn't want to disclose as much.

"No," I replied. "I'm good." The last thing I wanted to do was go out to eat and anticipate that he would pay. Even though I was sure he would, I couldn't take the chance because I came to Paris with a fabulous wardrobe, but virtually no money. The apartment was small and cozy. The front door opened onto a small living area and the kitchen, which was complemented by two large French windows. The kitchen and living area were divided by a rustic, dark-wood preparation table. A baguette, a cup of olives, and a few small pieces of fruit lay on the countertop. Two small chairs and a round table made for the only furniture, save for a loveseat, which Tristan informed me he made himself. Apparently, he was quite the handyman.

"So, what would you like to do?" he asked as he removed his coat and set down his motorcycle helmet. He then loaded an Eric Dolphy jazz CD into his player. The musician was playing the flute, and high-pitched runs filled the tranquility of the intimate space. I could smell a faint aroma of vetiver from an incense stick that had likely been burned earlier in the day.

"Well, I have a busy day tomorrow, but I'm really up for anything."

"Have you ever ridden on a motorcycle?"

I thought of the time when I was fifteen, riding around Jones

Beach in a bikini holding on to the ripped chest of a twenty-year-old at Greek Fest, the black fraternity beach party that all my teenage friends and I managed to scheme our way into. Alas, there was no need to bring that episode up now.

"No, not that I can remember," I lied. I reveled at the thought of riding around Paris in the middle of the night. It was so cliché, but that's exactly what we did.

I was wearing a short ruffled YSL-like purple taffeta dress, a black motorcycle jacket, fishnets, and a pair of uncomfortable but hot Louboutin booties. He put on his helmet, then put on mine, strapped me in tight, and hopped on his bike to ride into the Paris night.

It was 3 a.m. We sped down Rue St. Antoine through to Rue Rivoli, past Les Halles, and under the arch that led to L'Opera. The autumn air was crisp and the streets were empty and glowing from the streetlights. I tried to soak it all in, as I grabbed Tristan's torso, for security and a seductive embrace. We roared over the Seine and made our way down the Champs-Élysées and through the Arc de Triomphe with the steady hum of the moped vibrating between my thighs, and I was thrilled at the thought of my dress whipping around wildly in the wind knowing that the drivers behind me could see my panties as we swerved through traffic. We finally made our way to the Eiffel Tower and circled around the perimeter, staring at its golden hues from every possible angle. I couldn't believe I was there in that moment, falling for the romanticism of it all. Paris had me.

My mind was a stew of thoughts. Paris: check. Hot Guy: check. Romantic midnight motorcycle ride: check. Was I supposed to fuck him now? He was charming and nonchalant, whisking around those narrow streets effortlessly, in the dark, like some kind of punk-rock Romeo. I shifted in and out of consciousness, wondering if this was real, or a figment of my hyperbolic imagination. Suddenly the ride stopped. We were back at the apartment. He prepared his bed, took a few sheets and pillows to the couch, and went to sleep. I was left to sit, alone, in his room, on his bed, to contemplate the day's events. I was relieved that he had not made any sexual advances, yet I was also a little sad. Why was I being such a whore in my mind? Some French guy took me for a ride on his rusty moped around the streets of Paris, and I'm ready to give up the goods. How lame. I lay there clutching the pillow, staring at the ceiling, until I fell asleep.

~

The next morning I got up early to get ready for the fashion shows. After all, I was in Paris with a purpose other than getting laid by hot French guys. Luckily, the bathroom was inside his bedroom, so by the time he wandered into the bathroom with a pair of skimpy black underwear on, I was already dressed and primped for the day.

"Good morning," he said, his voice ragged with the first words of the day.

"Morning," I replied, giving him a full-body glance-over, while trying not to gawk. "I'm heading out early. I need to head over to Jardin des Tuileries for a show."

"No breakfast?" he asked. I declined. "Well, give me ten minutes, and I'll give you a ride."

So we hopped on his bike and sped off, making a stop at a boulangerie for a pastry before landing in front of a white tent in front of the Gardens. We wished each other well, promised to meet for dinner in the evening, and parted.

~

I scurried along the cobblestoned garden that led to the tents housing the shows in my five-inch Louboutin booties. It was a bad idea to wear those shoes because it slowed my pace down to negative-two miles per hour, but it was a necessary fashion choice. What was worse was that my invite didn't have a seat assignment, which meant only one thing. Standing room. I would be lucky if an editor didn't show up, so I stood in the back, scanning the room like a hawk, waiting for those last few moments before the stage screw pulled back the protective sheet from the runway to steal a seat. I spotted an opening in the second row, close to the stage just as the lights went down. As the models drifted down the runway my mind drifted toward Tristan. I should just do it, I thought. I'm such a whore for wanting to. I'm so lame for thinking I'm a whore for wanting to do it. I spent the entire show weighing the pros and cons of fucking this French guy. Part of me just wanted to be able to say that I went to Paris and got laid. And the other part of me wanted to fall truly, madly, deeply in love.

Dinner was at his apartment. Tristan surprised me by nonchalantly whipping up a salmon quiche and, for dessert, a Mirabelle and chocolate tart. So now this: a hot French guy who can cook. We ate dinner with limited conversation hampered by my inability to have an intellectual conversation in French. Then we went to bed. I kicked myself again, as I listened to him toss and turn on the futon just beyond the bedroom door.

We went on like this for three more days, until it came time for me to leave Paris. I had a 9:30 a.m. flight to New York, so there was no time for a leisurely breakfast along Rue St. Antoine. I was sitting at the edge of the bed when he walked in. He invited me to breakfast. I declined. I invited him to sit on the bed. He accepted. Fuck it, I thought.

We made love in the sweetest, quickest way we could. It wasn't earth shattering, mind-blowing, or even memorable. It was simple, utilitarian, and slightly affectionate. Like a peck on the cheek as you dash out the door for work. I wasn't thrilled but I was satisfied. And now I could tell my friends back home that I got my happy ending in Paris.

~

I returned to work at The Magazine Company the following week only to find that my coworker had been fired and my workload doubled. "Efficient," Mr. X had said to me as I looked sullenly at the stack of hard drives containing the five thousand or so images from fashion week that needed to be resized, optimized, and sorted for the top editors at all the magazines to leisurely sift through. "Valued," I heard him say amidst all the verbiage. The truth of the matter is that while the magazine editors were having a jolly old time spending money on lavish parties, oversees fashion spreads, and outlandish business-related expenses, like a shopping trip to Jeffrey's—for research, of course—magazine bigwigs were shitting their pants over huge advertising losses and dwindling subscriber rates. Boutique magazines were getting shuttered with a murderous axe, and staffers worked in the cubicles in constant peril of losing their jobs. So it was a no-brainer to fire one of two librarians, when one person could seemingly do the job for all twenty-five publications. I was livid, and seethed at my desk, skimming all of the airfare sales websites, plotting my next escape. Just then, the top editor from the number two magazine title called me. "Listen, I need all of Bill Cunningham's images from the Lanvin show for our spring preview issue. I need them right now," she pleaded in her lilting British accent. I rolled my eyes. How is it that a foreign accent can make the most outrageous requests and sound absolutely normal?

"We just got them in. It will be a few hours." I knew I could sort her images, burn a DVD, and give them to her within minutes, but I felt like making the bitch wait. Just because I could.

"Well, what does that mean? Two hours? Three? End of day?"

"I'll call you as soon as they're ready. It won't be too long, I promise." I smiled a fake smile into the phone and hung up on her. My thoughts turned to Abdoulaye. As cool and casual as I was on the phone, I was elated that he had thought to call me of all the other women He could have called. Did he think of me often? Was I his first choice? Or was I one among a long list of other women that he had likely called that day? I figured the latter, but secretly hoped for the former. I wanted to be the main one, as pathetic as that sounded. I wondered when, exactly, I turned from a sexy, fearless, independent young female, to a groupie, desperately grasping for any drop of a man's affection. What was the price I was willing to pay for any hint of love with these unavailable men? I didn't want to become one of those sad, middle-aged women that I saw in dance class, faithful, unconditionally loving vessels for money and sex.

"Broken." The phrase broke my train of thought. "It's fucking broken!" One of the tech guys from the information tech department was shouting, annoyed. I looked up from my cubicle to see the man walking briskly toward my desk waving a portable hard drive. "There's about five thousand high-resolution images from fashion week on here, and we can't connect the hard drive. We think an intern accidentally dropped it and damaged it somehow. What are we going to do?" I glanced at the drive.

"Oh, I backed those images up already," I responded nonchalantly. "We're good." I didn't need this job. They needed me.

~

I spent days and nights dreaming about Africa, wondering what it would be like to sway my hips on African soil the same way I did in class. So it was no surprise that I finally made my first journey to the motherland. I picked Senegal because not only had I fallen in love with Sabar, the country's national dance, but I also figured I could put my limited French to practice, despite Abdoulaye's mockery, if all else failed on the communication front. I told my boss at The Magazine Company that I would be taking three weeks off. They had no one else that could even remotely cover what I did in the office, so I didn't fear losing my job.

"Must be nice," Mr. X had commented, as he signed off on my timesheet. I planned to go to Ghana once with my church group. It never worked out though. Have fun."

AFRICA

Africa was a dream that became all too real as the days and months passed. I would listen to the drums in dance class and fall into a trance as I rode the rhythm onto a mythical dune across the sub-Saharan desert. This new land was my destiny.

I arrived not speaking a lick of Wolof, save for "Nanga def?", which any Sabar dancer roaming north of 110th and Malcolm X Boulevard in Harlem could have figured out was slang for "How you doin'?" God knows how far that phrase would get me in Senegal. There were a few people visiting from dance class for a workshop that another Sabar teacher was hosting, but I was never much of a tour person. I preferred to venture off by myself.

I found myself one early November morning standing hopelessly in a Dakar airport looking for a friend's relatives, whom I had never met, spoken to, or even seen before. I stood there in my bright-red Moschino pea coat like a blood-soaked flag in distress. It was the one item that I could describe that would be noticeable enough to my new family of strangers. I prayed that they would recognize me. Maybe that wasn't such a good idea. I attracted a steady stream of cab drivers, food vendors, and general riffraff looking for easy money from an obvious foreigner. I'm sure my brown skin and darting eyes gave them an extra dose of hope. But fortunately I had no local currency on me, so my admirers quickly fell away. After a short time of standing in the airport waiting, I got desperate and asked a driver to use his phone. But of course I spoke no Wolof, so he fielded the call to my hosts and they arrived shortly thereafter. The crew of two women—sisters—and another man, in his mid-twenties, anxiously waved to me as the crowd of Senegalese cabbies and hangers-on slowly descended upon me, Red Riding Hood in Dakar.

"I'm Yasmine," a diminutive, yet seductive chocolate-skinned beauty announced, while the others stood quietly beside her. "This is my younger sister, Soukeyna." She pointed to the innocent-faced girl.

"Hello." She waved shyly.

"I speak English—very little. But do you speak some French?" Yasmine asked.

"Un petit peu," I responded, in my weak French accent. If I were going to get by, I would need to step up my basic French, or at least learn some Wolof.

"Ah, okay! We can do this!" They all laughed together and pointed me to the parking lot where the hot air and red clay dust greeted me in the predawn hours of a Senegal morning.
The day had just begun and as the sun crept up over the buildings, the city began to come alive. The first fires lit by the street cooks cracked a bright orange against the Prussian blue dawn, and women laden with goods atop their heads paraded toward the markets. Cars honked endlessly as if to rouse any lazy person who dared to sleep late. And above it all was the steady hum of the morning prayers to bless the day's events.

By the time we arrived at the house, the sun sat comfortably in the east, casting lingering shadows in the archways of the buildings. Sheep baaed and chickens clucked at each other, ignoring the boundary lines of their pens. The house was two stories high, a cement façade painted a stark white, and the main level had a storefront used by the family for their tailoring business. The men working the store had just woken up and had their morning tea and were threading the machine for their daily work. The shop was exceptionally busy due to the upcoming holiday, Tabaski, because all the women in town were getting their outfits made. Inside the house we walked straight upstairs to a bedroom that I would be sharing with Yasmine. The house had glassless, arch-shaped windows with colorful fabrics shielding the rooms from the sun. The soft breeze that came through the openings was rich and welcoming, carrying along the constant sensual waft of burning incense called thiouraye, and charcoal from the women cooking outside. I set down my bags that were slightly wet from South African Airways having left my bags sitting on the tarmac in the rain in New York. Assholes. Luckily, most of the gifts that I packed were protected in plastic Ziploc bags. I had tons of magazines courtesy of The Magazine Company, and I handed those over, along with the piles of makeup, hair, and beauty products that I got for pennies at all the magazine beauty sales. The ladies of the house were elated. I, on the other hand, was completed deflated from my long-haul flight and quickly crawled into bed for a nap.

~

I awoke in what must have been the late afternoon to a

feeling of euphoria and intense hunger. Yasmine and Soukeyna must have heard me stirring in the bedroom because they immediately popped in to see their new sister and share the day's tales. Soukeyna, all of twenty, had just returned from her college classes and Yasmine had spent the day with her fiancé. I was flooded with a barrage of questions: How was your flight? How is New York? How is our brother? Are you hungry yet? What would you like to do?

I tried my best to answer all the questions, fully and excitedly, but I was still worn out from the long flight. The ladies took me downstairs to visit their brothers and cousins, the chief tailors, and left me there to silently observe them, while the evening meal was being prepared. Through the humming of the sewing machines, I watched as they created elaborate ruffles along necklines and shaped curvaceous silhouettes into dresses with no pattern in sight. The hazy sun flooded the small shop, gleaming through the soft brown dust, adding splices of deep red-orange to the already complicated graphics on the fabric. Within the hour, the men all took a break to have tea. One brother was in charge of the tea-making. It was such a wonderful moment of tranquility and stillness. He boiled the water. He steeped the tea leaves. He poured the tea into a glass cup. From this glass cup, he poured the tea into another, and he goes back and forth between the cups, a patient practice of an event duplicated many times, for many, many years.

After what may have been hours, but seemed like only

moments, Yasmine summoned me upstairs for dinner. It was an inviting plate of roasted chicken with onions, a kind of potato home-fries, and a salad. I noticed there was only one setting. Apparently, as a special guest, I was made to eat my meal alone, which they mistakenly regarded as privacy. As I ate my meal, I listened to the gregarious laughter and animated Wolof of the women just outside the room. A short time later Yasmine entered the room with a few watermelon slices. One of the brothers had gone to town earlier in the day and found one of the best melons at the market. I knew my stomach couldn't handle it, but I would try anyway. It just looked too good to pass up. I bit into its watery sweetness, and indulged in its illicit flesh. And then I threw it all up.

Yasmine rushed back into the room, to clean up the mess from the American guest with a weak stomach. The women looked on, worried that I would report back to their brother in the States of my misfortune. I could tell they were worried by the frantic looks in their eyes. I didn't care to tell on anybody, I just needed some rest. I thanked them all profusely, washed myself, and went back to sleep.

~

My ears opened before my eyes the following morning. Outside, the hypnotic chants of the morning prayers rang from the city mosques in the otherwise silent predawn. The voices joined in unison, in slightly different pitches, so that the sound created a haunting chorus to accommodate the sunrise in Dakar. I could hear the crowing of a rooster and the steady clucking of chickens, as the early risers began stirring in the streets. I lay there in peace. I still could not believe that I was in the Motherland and drifted back to sleep.

~

I woke up to an elegant tea setting for two, placed on the floor on a silver tray beside my bed. On the platter was a baguette, a plate with a fresh pat of butter, a jar of Nutella, and a silver flask of crème. There was a jar of Nescafé in between two dainty coffee cups. I felt like the little pauper in the story "The Little Princess", where she wakes up every morning to a feast that has appeared from nowhere. I was a bit embarrassed by the show of hospitality. I was, after all, just a plain girl from Brooklyn. Outside the room, I heard the soft murmur of several women speaking in Wolof, and the distant hum of sewing machines.

Even though I thought I would be spending some time around the house for a few days, the sisters had other plans. They did not want to pass up the chance to show off their new American friend. Yasmine happily escorted me into town. I soon gathered that this was Yasmine's cover for the chance to visit her various paramours, even though she was engaged to be her fiancé's second wife. We avoided the long public transportation ride and took a taxi. Our first stop was the offices of the national lottery.

Her lover was a senior official there and he often gave her money and gifts and took her out to eat. I sat in the dingy offices writing up a brief daily itinerary while they flirted and cooed in Wolof. "Do you have someplace I can check my e-mail?" I asked.

He quickly set up his workstation for me, and while I scanned my inbox, the two lovers made out in the corner behind me. I decide to e-mail my mom for a quick check in. Shing-I had e-mailed me to check that I arrived safely. I always welcomed her e-mails; they were like a friendly bird on my shoulder.

FROM: sxybrftdancer@yahoo.com
TO: tofubutter@hotmail.com
SUBJECT: Re: Are you alive?

Hey girl, I made it! It's so beautiful and WARM here in Dakar. Still a little tired. I'm just hanging out downtown, picking up some essentials, and taking it all in. The funniest thing happened on my way here. As we were walking in a busy part of town, we came to an intersection where there were literally hundreds--hundreds!— of men bowed down in prayer, right in the middle of the street. It was such a fantastic sight to see! Okay, write back, and talk soon. Xoxo

Then I scrolled down the list in my inbox: a few ads from my favorite shoe store, coupons, job offers, and junk mail. At the next entry my heart nearly leapt out of my shirt. It was from Abdoulaye. I had nearly forgotten that I sent him an e-mail two weeks ago because I never got a response.

FROM: drumdancelife@yahoo.com
TO: sxybrftdancer@yahoo.com
(No subject)

There are no fans or air conditioning in the dance class in Africa. It's called body conditioning. You Americans are so spoiled. I decided to come to Senegal. I needed a vacation. Call me when you arrive. 221-58-92-005.

The phone was beside me, right at my fingertips. I turned around and the two lovers were engaged in a hot and heavy make-out session, looking like two chocolate-dipped pretzels. The opportunity was there, but I decided against it. This was a call I needed to make in private. I shuffled loudly enough to cause the lovers to come up for breath. Her lover asked if we were hungry, and we agreed to go for lunch. Today we were eating at a local French café that was overrun with white European tourists. I ordered a hamburger complêt—a burger with a fried egg and fries tucked neatly under the bun—and a Coke.

While I ate lunch, I contemplated what I would say to him. My heart was racing, and all I could think about was getting back to the house so that I could make the phone call. The thought that he was here, in Dakar, made me restless, and I longed for a familiar face and an English-speaking voice, since my French was rudimentary at best and my Wolof practically nonexistent. Yasmine's lover agreed to give us a ride back to the edge of her town, where we would walk the rest of the way in, so as not to be detected by anyone that she might know. I walked quickly back to the house, a ten-minute walk made longer by the dead heat, red dust, and blazing sun that shone above us.

Outside the house, Yasmine guided me to a telephone shack across the street. A small goat stood guard outside its entrance. Once inside the small booth, I dialed the number. There was some static, and then a tone.

"Allo?"

"Hey! Do you know who this is?"

"Um. No. Enlighten me."

I laughed nervously. "It's your favorite student from New York. I just got your e-mail."

"Ah, okay. So you made it." His tone was more comfortable now. "How are you making out?"

"To be honest, it's so good to hear a familiar voice. I'm doing my best to communicate, but I don't know any Wolof!"

"That's okay. Where are you staying?"

"Guideway."

"Ah, Guideway. That's not far from me. Let me pick you up and take you around my part of town."

I was incredulous. This surely wasn't the same dancer I

knew from New York. But I agreed to the rendezvous. I wasn't sure how the women of the house would feel about this. I also had misgivings about visiting his family. Would they think that I was his concubine? I'd never personally met his wife, but I knew who she was, what she looked like, and that I sure as hell didn't pass for her. My Senegalese friend from New York had graciously allowed me to visit his family, but I think it may have been in the pretext of a possible engagement in the future. I approached the women with my proposition and did my best to diffuse the situation.

"My dance teacher from New York is staying in Pecine right now," I said in my choppiest French. "Would you mind if I visited his family tomorrow?" The women conversed among themselves and agreed that it would be a good idea to explore the city with a familiar face, and so plans were made for him and me to meet the following afternoon.

~

We arrived at Abdoulaye's family's house. The tall concrete walls were painted a crisp white and the building created an abstract silhouette against the stark blue sky and the red clay earth where we stood.

"How was your flight?" His voice was a welcome sound.

"Not bad. I flew South African Air. It had rained the day before, and the baggage guys left all the bags on the tarmac. My luggage arrived completely soaked on the outside."

"Oh, that's so typical. They're the worst. So, what is your itinerary while you're here?"

"Well, I hoped to maybe take a dance class, and visit Goree Island. I definitely want to get some fabric and a drum. By the way, here's the number of the family I'm staying with, just in case." He led me into the compound. The house was much like a rectangular box with the center cut out of it so that each floor had a view of the open space. There was a railing on every level outside the room doors so that you could walk out and either look up at the sky or down at the foyer. It was so simple, but stunning. He led me up three flights of stairs, until we reached the roof. There was a small goat attached to the building with a thick rope.

"Family pet. Are you hungry?" he asked. "My sister just made some lamb and okra stew. We call it Suppa Kandja." I nodded in agreement, and he disappeared to the lower level. I continued sitting on the roof, basking in the warm sunshine. From where I was, I could get a glance of the entire village as the people went about their daily business. Small children chased each other in circles rousing the red clay earth into clouds of red smoke around them. A lone ice cream cart rang a faint bell up and down the road, and I could see the man shaving some ice into a plastic cup and pouring colored sugar water on top, just like the vendors on 128th and Lenox in Harlem. There was also a lone goat tied to a pole on the roof, next to the freshly washed laundry. I wondered about her fate; she might very well end up as the main course of a Tabaski feast.

Abdoulaye crept up behind me. "The food is ready whenever you are." I jumped at the start of his voice. "I don't bite. Unless you ask me to." I smiled at his cheekiness.

"No, not right now. I think I'd just like to rest." I saw a room adjacent to the roof terrace where we stood. There was no door, only an opening to the room, which allowed the blazing sunshine to flood the space. A white mosquito net billowed above the bed and I opened its drapes to climb in and lay down. Abdoulaye followed me inside the room onto the bed, reached for his laptop, and searched for music to play. As the soft sounds of the mbira instrument began to flow into the room, I heard the unmistakable voice of Youssou N'dour. He lay down beside me and stared at my body. The way he looked at me sent shockwaves all over my body, but he never touched me. It was such a departure from the aggressive man that I had met at that ruckus Harlem party several months before. I was lying there, open and ready for him to take me and he wouldn't even touch me. All he did was stare as I drifted off to sleep.

~

It may have been seven or eight at night when I woke up because the sun cast a deep umber and lavender hue over the Senegalese landscape. I was hungry now, but my thoughts immediately bolted to my host family, and the worry they must have felt since I hadn't returned. He came into the room with a towel wrapped around his waist, smelling of Irish Spring and a fresh shower.

"My sister called your family. We told them you were sleeping and that you would come back tomorrow morning if you woke up too late. Is that okay with you?"

I felt a little awkward, but nodded as Abdoulaye opened the mosquito netting to hand me a tray of food that had been set aside for me earlier.

"I don't even have any clothes."

"You can wear something from my sister. You two are about the same size." He sat down on the bed behind me and straddled his legs around my sides. I dipped my spoon into the bowl filled with rice and covered with a thick tomato, lamb, and okra stew and caught a bit of each of the flavors in my mouth. The slimy okra slid down my throat and the salt and spicy peppers that filled the tomato sauce danced inside my mouth. I savored this filling meal as he sat behind me, watching each spoonful enter my mouth. As I ate, he rested his chin on the top of my shoulder, and grazed his lips against my skin. A mixture of grogginess and hunger consumed me so much so that I couldn't concentrate on the man, even though his lips felt electrifying on my shoulder. I finished my meal, and got up from the bed.

"That was really delicious. Your sister is a great cook."

"I will make sure I tell her."

"Do you have some towels? And maybe a sarong? I'd like to take a shower." The evening was just settling in, and my body was sticky and salty with dried sweat. The room was pleasantly warm, so a refreshing shower was just what I needed to cap off the night.

"Yes, I'll bring it to you. Go ahead in and take your shower." I stepped into the bathroom and turned on the shower faucet. The shower, like most others I had seen in Senegal, had no boundaries, so that the water seeped to all corners of the bathroom as I bathed. The cool shower was soothing, and I drifted in and out of consciousness as I lathered the soap over my naked body. I thought about Abdoulaye, and what was underneath the towel, which he had loosely draped about him. I knew that we would make love because our flirtation had been a long one. But I worried that the anticipation of what I was expecting might turn into a huge letdown. Maybe he didn't want to have sex with me at all, and this whole evening was a tease to make me want him even more. I turned off the faucet.

"Do you have that towel?" I yelled to Abdoulaye outside. I knew he would make me come for it.

"It's here, on the bed." I came out of the bathroom, nude and dripping wet. He stared at me, himself nude, under the mosquito net. He was typing on his laptop, and the glow from the computer screen highlighted his glowing dark skin and his hardened cock that lay on his thigh. I could smell the scent of burning incense, and there were two small tea lights that illuminated the otherwise dark room. He had left the door out to the roof open, so that I could see the night sky beyond the room.

"Let me dry you." I came toward him, my legs weak with longing and sexual anticipation. There was a fire that burned between my legs, and I wanted him to penetrate me, instantly, with no warning and no foreplay. I opened up the mosquito net, and he took my body into his arms and lay me down, hovering over me. There was a small calabash on the bed, and I could make out some shea butter inside. By now, the heat had dried my body and there were only a few remaining beads of water lingering on my skin. He took some shea butter in the palm of his hands and rubbed me firmly, starting with my breasts and nipples and ending with the soft spaces between my toes, until I glistened with the ointment. We breathed together in silence as he rubbed both of my thighs and, turning away from me, lifted my legs up so that he could reach the back of my legs and my butt. He rubbed broadly over my backside with both hands, before gently spreading my buttocks apart to lean down and lick my clit. I breathed deep as he took turns licking and sucking slowly, slipping his tongue deep inside me, so that I quivered with every motion. I could hear the soft sucking sounds as he sped up his licking motions, and I struggled to muffle my groans so that I wouldn't cause suspicion in the rest of the house. I wanted to scream in pleasure. He continued, nibbling on my protruding clit until I couldn't take it anymore and came. Even so, he didn't stop, and I grabbed his head, and asked him to stop, politely, but he kept at it, until I finally managed to leverage myself on top of him to slip his cock in my mouth. We pleasured each other until we both couldn't take anymore, and he straddled my backside, thrusting furiously, while tickling my clit. As he penetrated me I stared out the door into the black African sky, lit with blazing stars. Whether this was real, or a dream, the moment felt so perfect that I didn't want it to end.

We continued making love, trying new positions, and tiring ourselves until we fell on top of each other in a heap of fatigued satisfaction. I had no profound words to say, so I replayed the night's events in my head, over and over again, until I drifted to sleep.

~

I felt a wet, abrasive tongue stroke my cheek. Then another lick, only this one was firmer, and a horrible stench blew in my face. I opened my eyes only to be greeted by a curious goat, sniffing her newfound treasure. I turned over to question my lover, but the other side of the bed was empty.

"Um, hello? Is anybody there? Hello! There is a loose goat in here!" I didn't even bother to practice my limited French, not knowing the words for goat, scared, or loose. My lover glided into the room, unfazed, with a cup of coffee, powdered milk, and sugar. Despite my initial shock over the goat, the morning sun was magnificent, blazing a fierce light into the bedroom that awoke all of my senses. He smiled.

"Nescafé?" It was a welcome custom that I had grown to appreciate every morning. He set the cup of black coffee down on a silver tray. I watched him as he poured the powdered milk slowly into the cup, stirring the coffee to avoid lumps. From another small plastic bag he poured some sugar. He lifted the cup to my lips and I sipped my coffee, wrapped in a thin sheet, with my lover and the goat.

"Where are my clothes?" It dawned on me that not only had I spent the night, but must have also aroused suspicions in the compound. Surely they were wondering who this American woman was, who so boldly decided to spend the night in her male teacher's house. That they were likely familiar with his American wife unnerved me. For that moment, I felt guilty.

"My sisters did the laundry early this morning." He reached for a pile of neatly folded clothes that sat on a djembe in the corner of the room and handed them to me. I could smell their warmth and a sort of cleanliness that I had never seen even in the most sophisticated washing machines in the States. The fact that these women washed the clothing of their brother's mistress made me feel exponentially worse. One of his sisters called for him.

"Sheila is on the phone!" She shouted loudly, so that her voice echoed through the concrete walls. He jumped up immediately, and left me, alone, in his bed. It was then that I had my first moments alone, to contemplate what just happened. I felt exotic, sensual, powerful, and fearful because I did not know what this would mean for our relationship. It was something forbidden, but desired by so many women whom I saw on a daily basis back in New York. I felt like I just scored an incredible win, but one that I could not share with anybody. I couldn't even tell Shing-I because

I knew she would not approve. I was proud and ashamed all at once.

I glanced over on the bed and noticed his laptop was open to the playlist of songs that had been playing throughout the night. I was tempted to start the playlist again to help me recall the magic of the prior evening. I just didn't want him to know that I had prodded in his personal belongings. I was just getting to know him and didn't want to fuck up our dynamics.

But I was hungry for more information about this mysterious man. There was an open document behind the music playlist with the details of a Harlem apartment building. It had tons of pages, none of which I was interested in reading. I had remembered him mentioning something about real estate in passing, but I never got a chance to elaborate on the details with him. I was more impressed with the fact that this man was not only extremely attractive, but that he was an enterprising man, with a vision, and possibly a lot of money. Behind that document there were about three others, all open. I quickly scanned the documents, one after the other, and noticed a woman's name under scanned signature.

This surprising find was more of an interesting bit of information for me than a major source of intrigue. But I couldn't help feeling a tad jealous that this woman had already embarked on a huge endeavor such as a home purchase with the man I was just beginning to love.

I heard a slight shuffle of footsteps and quickly slid back to my space on the bed, feigning sleep. My lover walked into the room.

"You should get dressed. I just called your host family and they are expecting you. We'll take a cab." I slowly pulled myself up from under the covers, where I was warm and naked. Abdoulaye pulled back the mosquito net and climbed towards me to kiss me deeply on the lips. He continued kissing me, moving down my neck and over my breasts, where he lovingly caressed them with his lips. I pushed my body towards him, urging him on, and He complied by stroking me between my thighs with his tongue. He stopped mid-lick. "Get dressed."

~

When I arrived back at the house in Guideway, Yasmine and Soukeyna were busy preparing the daily meal of chebujen, a tasty dish of rice and fish with slow-cooked carrots, cabbage, and an array of pungent spices. Yasmine asked my lover if he wanted to join us for supper, but He declined, said a few pleasantries, and left.

~

The following day we had planned to set out early to visit Goree Island, where I would get to experience the slave museum and learn the history of Senegal's part in the slave trade. Yasmine and her fiancé took the hour-long trip with me to town, where we would catch a ferry to go to the island. It was an experience that I felt I needed to have, especially since so many of the women from dance class listed Goree Island as an essential place to visit once I got to Senegal. I was both excited and frightened at what I might encounter on the haunted island.

When we arrived at the dock, Yasmine tried hopelessly to get me a discount ticket for the boat ride. The woman at the ticket window looked at me skeptically, as I spoke very little and simply asked her for one ticket in Wolof. She asked me my nationality and I told her Senegalese.

"Canadienne!" she shouted.

"Je ne suis pas Canadienne," I replied to the woman at the ticket window, who would not allow me discounted entrance to Goree Island. Yasmine stepped in and started speaking in Wolof to the woman. I stood aside as she pleaded for me.

"I told the lady you were Senegalese and that you were my sister. But she won't believe me. So you will have to pay the international tourist fare." Defeated, I paid the cashier the higher amount and she handed me my ticket.

"I'm not even Canadian, I'm American!" I shouted to the lady in English as I walked away.

~

When we boarded the ship, all I could see was the crystal-clear water and the fantastically clear and sunny sky. As I took in a deep breath of sea salt, sunshine, and warmth, I felt incredibly blessed. Once we got to the island, I was completely enchanted by the beauty of the colorful buildings, the art, and the flora. The island reminded me of the Montmartre section of Paris, with all its quaint houses and cobblestone streets where I had spent a couple of afternoons having lunch on the lawn of the Sacre Coeur cathedral. The streets of the small village were arranged in the same French fairytale theme, and each corner was filled with artists, paintings, and other artisanal objects.

~

The actual slave house was at once terrifying and unemotional. The museum displays, the amount of people in this part of the enclave with video recorders (myself included), almost detracted from the seriousness of the place. But when I stole away to the quiet places—the room for the children, and the room for the little girls—I was haunted. Dimly-lit stone walls lined deep hallways with a few slivers for window openings. And finally, the Passage of No Return—a door opening directly onto the Atlantic—was a place where dead and punished slaves were thrown to the sharks. On the second floor of the house, I allowed myself to stand on the balcony and reflect on the sights and my emotions. As I looked down, I could see the opening of the Passage. How ironic, I thought, that the rocks and the water that lay before me so pristine and crystal-clear were once covered with the blood and flesh of my ancestors.

After visiting the slave museum on Goree Island, we took some time to frolic along the rocky coasts, and stare at the shockingly blue waters that sparkled under the blazing African sun. I was wearing a full-body swimsuit, but I was afraid to strip down in this Muslim country, less I came across as a crude foreigner. So I was content to walk barefoot along the shore, splashing my toes in the inviting waters.

As we sat on a bench, staring at the water, I couldn't help but think about Abdoulaye and the love we made. Or was it just sex? Maybe he was just incredibly good at giving good sex and making any woman believe that she was the one. I turned to look at Yasmine and her fiancé, who sat holding each other tight and occasionally kissing and whispering inside jokes to each other in Wolof. I knew that she had a lover in the city, and likely others around town, but this man that she clung to was her true love. I wanted to feel that kind of love. To be held, caressed, wanted, and treasured. Sex fulfilled my primal physical desires, but I longed to be truly loved by a man, passionately and indiscriminately. I wanted the intense lovemaking to translate into something bigger than what it was, but deep down inside I knew that I would need to look elsewhere for true love.

~

A week had passed and when I tried to reach out to Abdoulaye, his phone had been disconnected. Since the girls and I only went into the city about twice a week, I didn't have the chance to e-mail him to find out where he was. And with no cell phone of my own, I could only rely on the people in the house who owned phones, but gave me no privacy, or the makeshift phone stalls with their shoddy connections. It felt good to be disconnected from my highly wired world in New York City, but at times I felt completely depressed and isolated because of my lack of connectivity to my normal life, and, because of the language barrier, to the family that I stayed with.

I spent my remaining days replaying our lovemaking in my mind and wondering what my relationship with this man would be like once I returned home. Would the other women know that we had shared something in Africa? And how would He act toward me when I would come to class? Or maybe it was just a one-time shot, a fluke, a mistake.

I never got a phone call, an e-mail, or any other kind of communication for the rest of my stay in Senegal. I was sure our fling was over.

OUT OF AFRICA

When I returned to the States, I was somewhat altered and felt more like an immigrant than a native New Yorker. The cold, hard pavement felt surreal and I longed for the dusty clay roads and the smells of tchourie incense, lamb, and earth that seemed to permeate the Senegalese air. When I opened my lips to speak, I uttered Wolof and French, and struggled to find the simplest of English words. I was a foreigner in my own land, and felt strangely out of place sitting under the fluorescent lights that glared over my pitiful cubicle.

I opened a magazine and stared at a pale white woman in an awkward scarecrow-like pose. I thought it funny how so many young girls want to work in fashion. But most people don't see the ugly, senseless monotony of it at times. At first, it was grueling fun—going on fashion shoots as a lowly fashion assistant, fetching an Yves Saint Laurent dress for a Selita Ebanks shoot or waiting in the plush chairs of Van Cleef and Arpels to return priceless jewels for an accessories shoot. And then I hit the big leagues, or so I thought, at The Magazine Company, the company of my dreams, in a real nine to five job. I thought I made a huge leap through a vaulted door. Now, I was an ambitious kind of girl, doing what it took to make it in the cutthroat fashion media business. And finally, I was there, in the place I wanted to be, with nowhere to go. Granted, the job got me the cash to go to those places that I dreamed of as I pored over slick magazine pages. But as my focus began to shift from fashion to flying, I knew a part of me had already completed this phase of my life. Even the times that I spent entire days out shopping and hanging out, while checking into the office once or twice during the day did little to pique my interest in this dead-end job. More and more frequently I found myself coming to work and scouring discount ticket websites for fares. I would work overtime, saving, planning, and scheming for my next trip. I had mentally departed.

~

Since coming back from Dakar I began having sexual trysts with my Abdoulaye nearly every day. I would meet him in the early morning before work and we would do it in his apartment. Or sometimes we would go to a club or restaurant and fuck in the bathroom. Most often we did it in the stairwell of the dance studio, right before class since no one ever walked up the ten flights of stairs it took to reach the landing. A tinge of jealousy sprung up within me at the thought of another woman pleasuring Abdoulaye and I was angry with myself for feeling this way. I knew that he had other women, and I told myself that I could play the game just as hard—if not harder—than he did.

I would often get stares from the women in class, most notably an attractive, stealthy dancer, who tried her best to make my life difficult by standing in my way in dance class, stepping out of her space and on my feet, or slapping me with her wild arm gestures when we danced all-out. Most of all, she tried her best to make my life a living hell by calling and e-mailing me at all times of the day to talk about what I needed to do to promote Abdoulaye's classes. It annoyed me, but the truth of the matter was that I was having the time of my life traveling, being romanced by international lovers, and screwing the man who she claimed as her boyfriend. It was petty. It was immature. But it brought a sense of satisfaction to me.

Most of the other women watched quietly in amusement, or defended this woman as if she were some queen of the dance floor. She relished her admirers, but they were likely fucking her boyfriend, too. When I wasn't laughing at her, I felt sorry for the visible shame, jealousy, and embarrassment she must have felt every time a new woman came to class. She put on comical airs to prove her love and devotion for the man, who had clearly moved on from her and was using her to the point of abject slavery, robbing her wallet, her time, and ultimately her soul. I constantly reminded myself that I could not become her, that I was better than her, but deep down I knew that I was just as emotionally flawed.

~

Several more months passed at my job at The Magazine Company and my career was no further ahead than the first day I walked through the imposing glass doors. I sent several letters, pleading to anyone who would listen about my plight in a position that got me nowhere. Those with sympathetic hearts tried to refer me to mangers who had the ability to promote me, but mainly my wishes fell on deaf ears.

One summer morning I walked into work, up the escalator flanked by heartless waterfalls and dead art, past the new fashion assistant in her hard-won Victor & Rolf for H&M heart stockings and sweater, up the elevator with three editors who couldn't give a damn about anyone else, through the glass double doors, past my nondescript cubicle, and into the kitchen for my first cup of coffee. Staring at the espresso machine, I began to cry. Sob. I began sobbing. What was I doing? Where was I going with this? It became clear to me that I wanted to do this media thing. But I needed to do it my way, with my style, on my time. At that moment, I instantly stopped crying. I knew what I had to do. I knew that my time at this place was over. At that very moment, my boss, Mr. Z, walked in for his third dose of caffeine. I shifted my body away from him so that I could feign exhaustion by swiping my hands over my face to clear any remaining tears.

"Morning!" he chirped. "How's it going?" God. Why did he have to be so fucking chipper?

"Everything's great, Z." My smile was painful. "See you at the meeting this afternoon?"

"Sure!" And he continued prepping his liquid breakfast. When I got back to my desk, I began frantically searching for plane tickets to Paris.

"Hey!" I nearly jumped at the unexpected voice over the divider. It was Mr. Z. "If there's anything wrong, anything you'd like to talk about, just let me know, okay?"

"Okay, I will." As soon as he disappeared behind the other side of the glass doors, I whipped out my debit card, made a few clicks, and it was done. 9 p.m. flight the following Friday, Lufthansa, John F. Kennedy to Charles de Gaulle, one adult, one-way ticket.

The next day I scheduled a meeting, first thing in the morning, with Mr. Z. I dreaded it, but there was no turning back now. I had typed up my resignation letter, e-mailed it to Mr. Z, and mailed a hard copy to the office, for good measure.

"What's this?" Mr. Z looked at the e-mail, perplexed.

"I'm leaving. Next Friday will be my last day."

"Whoa, have you thought about this? What are your plans?"

"I'm moving to Paris."

"You're kidding me."

"No, I'm not." I showed him the e-ticket.

"Wow. Well. I personally think you're making a mistake."

"I'm sorry, I just don't feel that way."

"But I mean it's a steady paycheck for you."

"This just isn't for me."

"Is there anything that would make you reconsider?"

"A full-time, permanent position, and a raise. This is what I have wanted all along, but was never given the chance to have."

"Unfortunately, I can't offer you that at this time."

"Well then, my resolution is firm. My flight leaves next Friday evening." I listened to countless offers, though none was valid enough to make me stay. I didn't want any drama; I just wanted a quick exit.

I quietly packed my belongings and cleared my desk a little each day so as not to make a scene. Then, on the final day, all that was left was my desk and my computer. By then word got around and the entire staff began dropping by my desk, one by one, to say farewell. I told them that life has its sunrises and sunsets. The sunset at The Magazine Company had long gone, and was now drifting into a deep twilight.

~

My phenomenal job exit emboldened me with a sense of adventure and pride that I had never felt before. I had often taken risks in life, but walking away from everything I knew to go and live in another country was just about the most brazen thing I had ever done. Who knew what possibilities lay ahead in Paris? Maybe I could find some work at a graphic design house or do some freelance work at a fashion agency.

Even though Tristan had offered to host me for free at his place, my timing was a little off. He was currently hosting an ex-girlfriend and her two small children from Zambia. She had just gotten out of a bitter relationship with her children's father, and Tristan, being the ever-welcoming host, allowed them to stay.

"I couldn't say no. She has kids!" he pleaded with me. "But she will be gone by the end of July and then it will be possible for you to stay as long as you want." Even though I had to change my plane ticket, I was not fazed. In fact, the extra time would allow me to freelance, write, and save up some money for my extended holiday.

"How is August? I asked him over the phone.

"Parfait." Of course, I had concerns about leaving Abdoulaye back in New York, indefinitely. But what we had, I couldn't say was truly serious, although I knew there was a genuine affection there. Whenever I walked in the room, no matter who he was speaking to, he would always stop and glance at me—even if I was walking by without pause or comment. There was an electric chemistry between us, and everyone could feel it, much to the chagrin of the many other women who vied for his attention. When I told him that I would be taking an extended holiday he was furious.

"What the hell is in Paris?" he asked after a night of lovemaking. "Fucking French men."

"What's wrong with French men?"

"You! Fucking them!" I rolled my eyes at his dramatic display of jealousy.

"Do you really care? You have plenty of pretty young things to keep you busy while I'm gone. Get over it."

"You're a selfish bitch, you know that?"I nearly choked on my tongue.

"Are you kidding me? You're kidding me, right? You, with the fifty bitches on each side."

"Can you get the fuck out of my house? Right now! Before I call the cops." He said quietly but firmly. It had became his 'thing' to threaten to call the cops on me whenever we got into a fight. I laughed out loud. "The cops? Give me a break. If I told the cops all of the shit I've seen you do since I met you, you'd be in jail. I'm just being gracious because you have kids."

"Get out!" he barked.

PARIS, AGAIN

The flight to Paris was mainly uneventful. I sat alone, watching Bollywood movies and eating soggy rice pudding when I wasn't busy planning my itinerary for all that I would do once I arrived. I glanced across the aisle and noticed an equally bored black male, also disinterested in the unappetizing meal. This young man was handsome, with a slightly muscular build, and rich chocolate skin. He was dressed sharp in what I could detect was a Hugo Boss blazer, black slacks and a Piaget watch. I looked down at my own slumpy tracksuit and imagined that I looked like I came right off the streets of suburban America. We glanced at each other and smiled.

"You're not into the food very much I see. Me neither. I could go for a medium-rare steak and frites." I was charmed at his easy-going demeanor, and surprised that he hadn't mentioned his mother's cooking as his main culinary desire.

"Not exactly. It's not horrible, but I would really love a tartine and a café au lait. I guess I'll have to settle for the chai," I joked.

"My name is Fola." He reached out his arm for a hand-shake and we exchanged niceties. "I'm doing some business in Paris for a few weeks and then headed off to Germany. What are you doing in Paris?"

"Oh, nothing important. I'm on holiday actually." *Holiday.* It sounded so European and snobbish. I hoped my use of the word didn't turn him off.

"Holiday. Must be nice," he laughed. "Hey, let me give you my number. Maybe we can connect when you get settled."

He scrawled his number on an airline napkin and handed it to me. "For sure. I'll definitely give you a call sometime."

~

I disembarked my flight on a Saturday morning when Paris was still asleep and I could walk the streets, ragged and unglamorous, with my stack of luggage in tow. Tristan's apartment was in the heart of Bastille, a lively section of the city filled with cafés, boutiques, and large-scale stores catering to English-speaking tourists. I struggled down Rue St. Antoine to the apartment, and passed several eateries, but decided to drop my luggage off first. Food could wait.

When I arrived at the house, I punched in the code for the front door, and lugged my huge suitcase up the three flights of the narrow staircase. I stood in front of the apartment door, and this time found the key under the door, just as we had arranged. I opened the door, half expecting to find the house in complete disarray with kids' toys and Tristan's ex-girlfriend, but the apartment was empty. I walked in and dumped my enormous suitcase on the living room floor and felt at home. I stripped off my travel weary clothes and immediately headed to the bathroom for a shower. Tristan was at work, so I could enjoy the wonderful midday sun in the apartment. I tied on a light sarong, perfect for the summer heat in Paris, and curled up on the living room sofa for a nap.

After what could have been hours, I woke up to a pair of

voices in the room. I was sleeping facing the wall, but I could make out Tristan's voice, and the voice of a woman. I remained still as if I were sleeping. It was the girl he was currently seeing. I think he said her name was Emiline. They were arguing in hushed tones, and went into his room and shut the door, where they began arguing louder. Before I came, he told me that they were on the rocks, and had been fighting every day. He wanted to be done with her—or so he said—so he didn't mind if I decided to visit for a while. It was his apartment after all, and she had her own just outside the city. I knew I was playing with fire, but I came anyway. I wasn't in Paris to start shit; I wanted a break from the craziness of New York City, and a chance to refresh my creative juices. Little did I know that Paris had its own brand of crazy.

While they were in the bedroom, I took the opportunity to get up and start moving around the kitchen, and making some noise, so that they would know I was awake. I made myself a cup of coffee, and sat on the bar stool in front of the kitchen island. After a few minutes, they both emerged from the bedroom. Tristan look exhausted, but I couldn't make out her expression. Was it anger? Disdain? Jealousy? She looked at me in my skimpy sarong, with a hint of lip-gloss, and disheveled hair twists, sipping my café au lait like I didn't have a care in the world. I looked like I just emerged from a night of great sex.

"Hi, nice to meet you," I greeted. I knew she wasn't too thrilled to see me there, so I camped up my excitement at meeting her. I beamed from ear to ear, as I looked her over. Not very impressive, I thought to myself. She was barely five feet, and wore the most uninteresting flats, jeans, and a horrible old T-shirt. Her skin was a dark-olive tone, and she wore no makeup, and no jewelry. Her mousy look was accented with a pair of librarian-worthy black-frame glasses, and a tight bun. She was not ugly. She seemed like one of those women that could be transformed into a complete vixen with the right tools.

"This is my friend Emiline," Tristan said, breaking the awkward silence. Emiline smiled, annoyed. I don't think she was too happy being referred to as a friend. And she couldn't have been too happy to see some brazen American chick wrapped in a sarong in her so-called boyfriend's house. I could see that my presence was a big reason why they were arguing.

"We should go out for drinks," she offered. "I know several great spots around here. This is kind of like the club part of town." Her broken English was light and almost charming. She was a simple girl from what I could see, but she definitely had a bitchy side from what I could discern.

"Sure, why not. I need to learn the intimate parts of the city," I replied, feigning excitement. The last thing I wanted to do was to get inebriated with the sometimes-girlfriend of Tristan only to inadvertently blab some sordid details and come into the middle of a firestorm. He was my only real contact in Paris, and if I fucked things up, I would have to go home early.

"I'm taking Emiline to work, and I'll be back, Tristan said. "Make yourself comfortable." I nodded, and they left. I sat there in the living room wondering what exactly had I gotten myself into. I was smitten with Tristan, and while I was in America, I often fantasized about what it would be like if I began a relationship with this Frenchman. What if we took things further? What if I married him? What would our kids look like? I was getting ahead of myself. I dressed and went outside to grab something to eat.

~

I came home a few hours later to find Tristan sitting at the kitchen island, eating olives and contemplating. The air was heavy with contempt.

"Hey," I said, breaking the uncomfortable silence. "How was your day?" I knew he had a shitty time with Emiline, but I wanted to try and lighten the mood.

"Not too good. Emiline and I—we are taking a break. It's too stressful. She is studying right now for a huge test, but with her, there is always something. She's never satisfied, and the good times that we do have are becoming less and less . . ." he trailed off.

"I hope me staying here isn't going to give you any more stress." That was a lie. I knew damn well that for Emiline, the very presence of another woman around Tristan—living in his apartment, no less—was a major point of contention at this time in their relationship. But, again, my own selfish needs overruled a more reasonable option, which would have been to stay at some other accommodation.

"No, don't worry, it's not a big deal. It's not like she lives here. We've just decided to remain friends for the moment. We just need to be apart for a while. Have you eaten?"

"I had a sandwich earlier, but I should be having dinner soon. My body is still adjusting to the time switch." He poured me a glass of red wine and sifted through his CD collection. I had just noticed that his entire wall was crammed with CDs, old records, and cassette tapes. He was a music junkie. Upon closer inspection, I noticed that they were an eclectic mix of classical, world, jazz, and soul records. Aretha. Nina. James. Fela. Yo Yo Ma. He selected a CD and popped it into the player. There was the sound of a crackling record, and a tinkling of the piano keys, followed by the sultry, rich, unmistakable voice of Sarah Vaughan singing "April in Paris."

"I wanted to make lasagna bolognaise. Have you ever had it?" He asked over the music.

"Yes, I think it's like an even meatier version of regular lasagna. I'd love that." While he cooked, I unpacked some items, and sorted through some stray papers. When I finally felt settled, the food was ready. Tristan arranged two table settings, poured some wine for us, and we sat down to eat. Then his phone rang. It was Emiline. He put his finger up to signal that he would only be a moment, and went into the bedroom.

I sat at the table alone, staring down at a delicious plate of lasagna. Tristan had also taken the time to set a small plate of appetizers: some oysters, sun-dried tomatoes, olives. It was simple, yet elegant, and not at all contrived. It just all felt very relaxed and natural. This was what I was looking for in Paris. After a few minutes, Tristan came back out, a little agitated.

"Dinner looks great," I said.

"Bon Appetit."

~

It was time for bed and once again, we came upon the conundrum of my first visit. There was a sexual tension in the air, but we didn't know how to express it without the moment seeming forced. Tristan once again offered me his bed, agreeing to sleep on the couch. We lay on our respective beds for what seemed like ages. Tristan finally walked into the room.

"I can't sleep," he said.

"Me either," I laughed.

He walked toward the bed and fell softly on top of me. We kissed and grabbed at each other with a ferocious hunger. It had been too long. He licked and sucked my neck, and I writhed in pleasure as he lifted my shirt with one hand and pulled down my panties with the other, kissing my breasts at the same time. I wanted to start on him, but before I had the chance, he pinned my arms down under my thighs while tickling my navel with his tongue and before I knew it, he was sucking and nibbling on my clit with eager lubriciousness. We fucked all through the night until we fell asleep simultaneously, into a heavy slumber. If this was what my nights in Paris would be like for the next few months, I was game.

The next morning, Tristan woke early to go to his artisan job in the center of the city. He had a part-time gig designing sets for plays, a job which he enjoyed because it offered him flexibility to do his own projects, and the salary to fund them. His part-time employment as an artisan also gained him several government subsidies like special discounted entertainment and compensation when he didn't work. He truly lived the artist's life and I was in love with the concept.

While he was out, I had devised a loose plan to learn all about Paris, all the while maintaining my reading and writing. I felt like I needed a rejuvenation of the senses and I set out to exercise my mind, body, and soul in as many ways as possible. I got dressed and set out for the Marché d'Aligre, the local fresh-food market that I read was inexpensive and full of variety. Luckily, Tristan left me a pass to use the Velib, a public bicycle system all around central Paris. With my map and a bike, I planned to conquer the city.

~

Tristan and I were getting along nicely in our tight quarters. Every day he left for work early, and I was able to go outside for a fresh croissant and a coffee, and lounge around and catch up on the news and write. I couldn't believe that I was actually living the mythic artist's life in Paris. The only nagging element was his girlfriend, Emiline. Actually, I didn't know what the hell was going on with them. Were they a couple? Were they over? They fought nonstop. Tristan would make dinner and we would sit down, and she would call and engage him in a long-ass conversation that would inevitably piss him off. He would leave the table, frustrated, only to come back and eat dinner an hour later. I loved the thrill of being with Tristan, but this romantic drama was more than I had bargained for.

~

Tristan had to go out with his father to work on the set of an independent movie by an underground multimedia artist. It was a low-paying gig, but Tristan loved immersing himself in offbeat projects that had potential. He was a true artist at heart.

"I'm not going to be around much today. Why don't you go out with Emiline? She's not studying tonight, so I think she would love to have some company. Let me call her up."

He hadn't dialed four numbers on his cell phone before the doorbell rang. It was Emiline. What the hell! Was she psychic or something? I really wasn't prepared to see this chick right now. I had my own plans for scouring the town solo.

"Hi!" She waved from the door, perkily. Tristan was taken aback.

"Wow, I was just going to call you."

"Oh, I was in the neighborhood." *Stalker*, I thought. "I'm not studying tonight. I need to get out! Would you like to come out with me? There are lots of really cool bars in Bastille. I'm sure we can find one." She was no longer wearing her mousy glasses, and she had taken the time to line her eyes with kohl and apply a bit of rouge. Her hair was down—a change from her severe bun. She wore a tight white sweater, low slung dark denim jeans, and open-toe sandals. She was studying me hard, angry that I was living in the same apartment with her supposed boyfriend. I didn't want to hang out with her. She was certainly not one of my girlfriends, and I didn't care to become friendly with her. She had an agenda that was quite plain to me, yet not obvious to Tristan. No, I didn't want to be her friend. And the last thing I wanted to do was get wasted at a bar and accidentally divulge how fantastic Tristan's oral was.

"Sure!" I replied.

"Great! There's a few bars not far from here." She turned to Tristan. "How long will you be with your father?" She asked this in French. This pissed me off for two reasons. One, Tristan spoke with her already, so she knew his plans, and second, the bitch thought I couldn't understand her. I mean, we were all speaking English, so what was the point of switching up all of a sudden? *Bitch.*

As we headed out the door I noticed she tried to kiss him when I wasn't looking, but he rebuffed her and threw on his helmet. Whether it was a ploy to throw me off or his genuine dis-affection, I wasn't too sure, but the whole scene was pretty pathetic.

Anyway, I was more concerned with figuring out how I would enjoy a night of drinking without having any disastrous effects on my stay in Paris.

Emiline wobbled down the cobblestone streets in kitten heels. I had on a pair of stiletto booties and tight Levi's with an African-print halter-top. Sexy was my typical uniform, and I wasn't about to get shown up by a mousy French woman. I was looking for an interesting bar, but I could feel Emiline staring me up and down, studying me. I turned to her suddenly, catching her off-guard.

"Let's go to this one." I spotted a trendy-looking club called Tribar, among a strip of neon-lit storefronts teeming with young tourists and college students. I figured if I found a club that was lively enough, it would avert attention away from any conversation that I would be forced to have with Emiline. We sat down at a high table surrounded by beautiful young people smoking cigarettes.

"Do you smoke?" she asked me.

"Oh no, it's not my thing." No reason to mention my few drags from the weed pipe every now and then.

"What would you like to drink?"

"Maybe a sangria?" I asked. I know it's typically a Spanish drink, but New York City had everything, so why wouldn't Paris?

"Sangria? What is that?"

"Oh, it's really good. Red wine with lots of fruit. Maybe

they don't have it. You know what, I'll take a Kahlua and milk. Everyone has Kahlua." Emiline ordered for me and ordered a glass of white wine for herself. When I reached for my wallet she refused.

"Don't worry, you can get the next one." We laughed and proceeded with cringing niceties. The waiter came back with our drinks and I gladly took a sip. I needed this to be as painless as possible.

"So . . ." I started. "Tristan told me that you are studying to be an international flight attendant. Must be exciting, being able to travel all over the place."

"Yes, it's a really hard test. I've been working with Air France for about a year now, but the real money comes with the international flights." Her softly broken English was disarming. I let go a little.

"I love traveling. I try to come to Paris about two or three times a year."

"Oh wow. I love this job because I get free flights everywhere." I smiled. *Bitch.*

"So, how did you meet Tristan?" Emiline asked.

"Through a mutual friend in New York. We are all artists you know. We are all in the same circles."

"So . . . you met for the first time in New York?"

"Well, no, we met here. My girlfriend was here with me and introduced us," I lied.

"Wow, Tristan has so many international friends. I wonder

if I know her."

"I'm not sure you know her." I thought of Gwenyth. "But they have known each other since childhood."

"Oh really, Tristan never told me about her. What was her name?"

"Gwenyth. She's a sweet woman. We dance together in New York." I sipped my Kahlua.

"Dance? What kind of dance?" Good Lord. She probably thought I worked the pole, King of Diamonds-style. I took a sip of liquor through the straw.

"We do traditional African dance. I was actually looking for some dance classes while I'm here in Paris."

"That is interesting. I am from Tanzania. We have our own style of dance. I can show you sometime." We both laughed at the idea.

"Yeah, I plan to dance, study, and write while I am here in Paris."

"Oh okay. So . . . you aren't working while you are here?"

"No, I'm just on holiday." She shuffled uncomfortably in her seat a little. "Wow. How fun. How long is your vacation?"

"Oh, I'll just be here a couple of weeks." Months. A couple of months, I thought.

"Well, you came at a good time. It's quiet in Paris—everyone is on holiday." I smiled and took another sip of my cocktail. "So. What do you think about Tristan?" I was almost finished with my cocktail, and I shuffled the ice in my glass. "I can get you another," she offered. Oh hell no, bitch. *You are not going to get me wasted so I can spill all the details on this man.* She didn't even finish her glass, and we had been sitting in the bar for about thirty minutes now.

"Oh, you know what? I'll just take a glass of water." She summoned the waiter and ordered a bottled water for me. Here we go. I knew where this was going, and I was going to keep this as simple as possible without giving up too much information.

"Oh, he's great. Very smart. He has a great music collection. Some rare Ella Fitzgerald and Charles Mingus pieces. Great stuff." She nodded but I could tell she wasn't familiar with them.

"Yes, he's very talented. And he is handsome, don't you think?" She sighed. I tried hard not to roll my eyes. "Yes, you got a great catch!" I answered.

"Oh, we're not dating. We decided to call things off. It's probably for the best, you know?"

"Sure, I replied, and took a final sip of my cocktail. "Listen, I have some writing to do tonight. Would you mind if I take that water to go?" As I walked out of the door with my Evian, I glanced at her from the corner of my eye, sitting alone, slumped sadly at the bar, defeated.

~

I woke early the next day with a list of early-morning activities. I wanted to go to the market, take a short bike ride into town, and visit the Museum of Fashion inside the Palais Galleria. I was just about ready to step outside the door when the phone rang.

"Hello?"

"Hi there, it's Emiline!" What could she possibly want at this time of the day?

"Oh hi! How are you?" I really didn't care, but I didn't have a good reason to be mean.

"I'm fine. And you?"

"You know I was just about to step out the door, actually."

"Ah, I see. Did Tristan already leave for the day?"

"Yes, he did as a matter of fact. He left a little earlier than usual. He said he had some work to do before the opening of the show he has been working on. I'll tell him you called."

"Okay, thank you." I was just about to hang up when she called my name. "What are you doing today?"

"I have a long list of things to do as well as some research, and other small errands. Did you need something?

"Oh, I was thinking that maybe we could visit the Mosquée de Paris. Have you been?"

"I'm not Muslim," I responded flatly.

"It's okay, there are many things to do and see inside the mosque. They have what is called a hammam inside where you can relax. I can explain it to you when I see you." I was intrigued. Even though I wasn't keen on hanging out with this woman—who wanted be my friend, but was clearly my enemy—I was more interested in visiting a new place in the city. I agreed and we met a half an hour later at the carousel that sat in the town's intersection off the Boulevard Beaumarchais.

Emiline was dressed simply this time in plain black capris, a slim T-shirt, and flats. She wore her hair in her signature bun, but no glasses. I detected a hint of eyeliner, and her lips were stained a berry red. At least she was making a better attempt of looking attractive, even if she came off as a poor girl desperately trying to hold on to a failed relationship.

"You are going to enjoy this." She seemed genuinely excited. "All the women in Paris go to the hammam. It keeps your skin beautiful. There are several steam rooms inside, and you can get a massage. I think you'll really like it." We got off at the Place Monge stop on the Metro and walked around a few rounded streets until we found the Mosquée de Paris along a quiet street adjacent to the Botanical Garden. After touring the intricately designed courtyard outside the main corridor, we went inside the mosque, and to the side was a slightly hidden door, where several women sat beyond its secretive doors. I gathered that they had just finished enjoying their spa, as they were leisurely sipping on mint tea. Beyond the front foyer was a thick door, further covered by a black curtain that led to a large circular room, ornately decorated with intricate mosaic tile that faded at places to reveal the building's age. Emiline and I paid for the hammam entrance fee as well as a body scrub, massage, and tea. We were instructed to remove our shoes and head to the back locker rooms to remove all of our clothing save for our bikini bottoms.

The air was heavy and thick, filled with nude women lounging across vinyl mattresses covered with towels. In the center were several massage tables where thick Middle Eastern women worked feverishly, slathering an array of oils onto limp bodies. Several women lounged and drank tea as they waited for their massages. Past this room was another, darker room, where women were taking showers and receiving their salt scrubs. Even farther back was another room, whose steam was so thick that I could only faintly make out the bodies of bathing women. The scene was just short of a harem, without the sexual element.

As we undressed in the locker room, I couldn't resist sizing Emeline up. Despite my bravado, I was still a little insecure about my body and how I compared with her. What did Tristan see in her that made her attractive? My curvaceous frame was a far cry from her petite delicate features. Her body was a rich taupe, lithe, and unblemished like that of an adolescent girl. Was there a type that he liked? Was he sick of her type and wanted someone with a little more meat? Maybe I was just his international treat, and I was just being played. I pondered these thoughts as we put our belongings in a locker and went to the bathhouse located in the back of the hammam.

The center of the room was filled with an ice-cold marble pool, where women dipped in and out to cool their bodies off from the impossibly hot air. There were naked bodies everywhere, and I admired the women as they lay, languidly among each other, uncaring of their nudity. It was incredibly liberating to feel free and uninhibited in my flawed nakedness among the other French women who thoughtfully labored on their own bodies in the steam rooms, massaging, scraping, and sloughing their skin to radiant perfection.

The hammam was like taking a trip back in time, as I watched the women of various body types, reclining languidly around the rooms like variations of a classic Renaissance odalisque painting. There were waterspouts at intervals around the room, and women lined up with buckets to cool themselves off with the waters.

"Tristan loves when I come here because I always have a glow when I leave. The steam is very healthful."

I nodded sympathetically, but I really couldn't talk to her. I couldn't even look her in the eye as she talked about him because I had been fucking him all this time. I don't know if it was shame or pity that kept me close-mouthed. I glanced at her body once again, this time focusing on her breasts. They were small but supple, with nipples only a touch darker than her skin and their soft roundness reminded was reminiscent of a virgin's innocence. I thought of a Naomi Campbell quote, where she had said that the perfect sized breast should fit inside a champagne cup. Compared to Emiline's breasts, mine were borderline porn star. I looked down at my chest, their large, dark areolae announcing my womanhood. She looked pure and vulnerable, untainted, but longing for love. As she confessed her adoration for Tristan, I gazed at her, and wondered how she made love to him. Was she shy? Did she take charge once the doors were closed? Was she a screamer?

"We stopped having sex weeks ago." Her candor jarred the relaxed mood of the spa atmosphere. Emiline was looking down at herself, in pity. "I wanted to make it work, but his heart wasn't there." I wasn't quite sure what to say in this situation. Do I offer her words of encouragement despite the fact that I wanted Tristan all to myself? Do I openly confess my infatuation for her man?

"If it's meant to be, it will be. I wouldn't stress it. You know how fickle men are." I finally answered.

"I guess you are right," Emiline responded, feebly.

"Hey, let's not talk about men. We're supposed to be enjoying ourselves." I got up from the stone bench and headed for the adjacent room. "I'm going to get my grommage. Wanna join me?" I asked her, as we watched two thick Turkish women roughly slough the bare bodies of their moist clients with dark pumice.

"That sounds nice," she replied, flatly.

~

One night Tristan decided to surprise me with his version of boeuf bourguignon with half the steps of the original recipe. It was his favorite, and he had used an ancient cookbook, about six hundred pages. He cooked feverishly, chopping, simmering, and tasting the concoction that he had created with the fresh ingredients I purchased from the Marché d'Algiers earlier in the day. The apartment smelled delicious. Tristan pulled out a bottle of deep red wine, and poured us each a glass. We sat at our small kitchen table and nibbled on olives and soft cheese, drinking our wine while we waited for the dish to finish cooking in the oven. I lit a tea-light candle and set it on the table, for ambiance. Finally, we sat down to enjoy the fruits of his labor, with Tristan spooning the meal artfully onto his artisanal china. Just as I put the fork to my mouth, the phone rang. We both sighed, annoyed. We knew it was Emiline. Tristan looked at the phone.

"Tristan, come on. We're eating," I sighed. This was the perfect meal and I was not about to have it ruined by a woman who wouldn't let go. Or maybe it was Tristan who wasn't allowing her to let go. Either way, I was in no mood for a threesome. This bitch always seemed to know when we were sitting down to eat.
"I know." He stared at his cell phone in a foreboding way. "It will be quick, I promise."

I rolled my eyes as I watched him walk from the kitchen to the couch to the bedroom, and back again. She would not let up and she was certainly not going to let me win. This was her game, and her territory. After about an hour, Tristan emerged from the bedroom, deflated. He sat down to eat his cold dinner, and I watched him from the couch, while I read a magazine.

"Is this how it's going to be Tristan? How can you continue talking to her if she frustrates you so much?"

"I don't know. I just can't deal with her. We aren't together, but then she fights with me like we are."

"Well, you obviously still love her. Otherwise, you wouldn't waste your time. Just be honest with yourself." He didn't answer me. "I'm going to bed."

After a few moments, he came to bed with me, and we lay quietly, staring at the ceiling. He was frustrated, and I reached to kiss him. He turned away. I tried to wrestle him playfully. Angry, he got up and went into the living room and fell asleep on the couch. I lay there in the dark, alone. I couldn't sleep, but I didn't move. I listened for his breathing as a sign that he was sleeping. He tossed and turned on the couch. After an hour, I heard the door click as he slipped out of the apartment.

~

I woke up the next morning to a cold and empty bed. I went to the living room to see if he had come back while I was sleeping. The apartment was empty. I went back into the bedroom and sat on the bed, dejected. I didn't know if I was angry or heartbroken, but I felt pitiful, and I cried, naked, on the bed. I knew where he had gone. He had left me for Emiline. I felt used, played, and foolish for allowing this man to have a piece of my heart, when he clearly had affections for the woman he spoke so badly about. I blamed myself for getting into this messy situation. I should have left him alone.

I scrambled through my agenda and found the phone number that Fola had e-mailed me. I called his number and he gave me his Amsterdam contact information. He said that he would be there for a short while, and that he would get me a return train ticket. I was skeptical of the whole idea, until he sent me the money via Western Union to go buy my ticket. It was then that I knew he was for real. I needed this break from the drama in Paris. I wanted to be away from Tristan, Emiline, and any French men for the moment. I just wanted to take my mind off it all and have a good time.

Fola swiftly wired the money to the nearest post office, so that I would be able to get my train ticket at Paris Gare du Nord station before they sold out. After I got the money, I hopped on a Velib and took a ride to nowhere, tears streaming down my face. I rode through the seedy, graffiti-scrawled Barbés section, down through Belleville's Chinatown, in a sea of sadness, confusion, and anger. I hated Tristan. As I pedaled furiously down the Boulevard Beaumarchais, I repeated to myself over and over: Fuck him, FUCK him, FUCK HIM.

DETOUR IN AMSTERDAM

The first time I took a train cross-country, I was thirteen. It was quite an elaborate trip, given the fact that we could have simply taken a quick flight from London to Paris. But my mother's friend Elaine had booked an excursion for us which included a charter boat across the English Channel. We barely endured the choppy waters due to motion sickness. I suffered bravely managing to only get a headache, while my mother stayed hovering over a toilet bowl. At one point, I remembered a gentleman in a suit and tie running hurriedly to a bathroom to vomit. It was an awful scene of sick passengers and slipping silverware. After the horrendous boat ride, we docked in the Port of Calet in France where we took a bus to Paris. In college, I opted for a less adventurous route by hopping on a Eurostar, and for the trip from Paris to Amsterdam, I did the same. By now, I figured that a five-hour ride between these two cities via Brussels would be a cinch. I had my Louis Vuitton duffle bag and my oversized black Marc Jacobs quilt tote to handle my stuff. I wore my trusty leather bomber, leggings, a pink Sonia Rykiel tank, and some booties. I was cute enough to be attractive, but sporty enough to make a dash, just in case things went south. I was ready for anything.

~

As I daydreamed of running across the narrow Dutch canals, dipping in and out of whorehouses and eating pot brownies, I drifted into a soft slumber. No sooner had I fallen asleep than I was abruptly woken up by three national-security agents. Two men and one woman, wearing blue jackets with CIP emblazoned on their backs. They screamed at me all at once.

"Madame! Madame! What is your destination?" they barked in French.

Red-eyed, I sat up in my seat, slurring my words. My hair twists were strung every which way over my head. With my bomber half covering my face, I must have looked like a pothead. They demanded my bags.

"I'm going to Amsterdam," I replied in English. "What is this about?" By now all the passengers in the car were staring at me.

"Random checks. Please stand up." The woman patted me down, as the men dumped the contents of my bags on a seat and sifted through them. "Where are you from?"

"I'm from New York, but I was staying in Paris for holiday." She gave me an uneasy side eye as she scanned my passport and travel documents.

"Okay. She's clean. Sorry miss. Have a good day."

I just stared at the three agents as they shuffled off, my shit skewed all over the aisle. This little trip could only get better from this point on.

~

The train finally pulled into the Centrale Station in Amsterdam. As I walked down the corridor looking for Fola and his cousin, Celé, I couldn't help but be a little worried. Here I was, once again in a foreign country, on my way to meet and stay with people I barely knew. Only this situation was a bit more precarious; I had only met Fola on the plane to Paris a few weeks earlier, and really knew nothing about him. He could be one of those Nigerian scammers that you read about in the papers all the time. I guarded my passport like it was the Blue Diamond. I saw them standing in the crowded terminal, leaning against a pole. Fola looked as fine as I remembered, wearing a fitted shirt, slouchy jeans, boots, and a newsboy cap. His shirt nicely displayed his well-defined pecs in a subtle way that was not at all cheesy. I watched as he talked to his cousin, slightly less built, but equally as handsome. He bit his heart-shaped lips as he conversed, and I knew I made the right decision to visit. It was a welcome diversion from all the drama in Paris.

"Fola!" He caught sight of me and smiled. "I made it!" I gave him a hug and greeted his cousin.

"I'm so glad you're here. To be honest, I didn't think you would come."

We walked farther down the corridor until we were standing outside of Centrale Station. I told them about my run-in with the enforcement officers on the train.

"Ah, the Criminal Investigation Police. Always picking out the brown-skinned people. Racists! Never mind them. So, do you want to walk around a bit? Or do you want to drop your bags off first?"

"To be honest, I'm a little hungry. Can we get something

to eat?" It was very early in the afternoon, so many of the tourists were out with their families. Scores of young children ran along the cobbled streets and vendors sold cheesy Dutch souvenirs along the main drag. I settled for a bag of Frites and sauce.

"Can I hold your bags?" Celé offered.

"No thanks, I got it." These guys seemed cool, but there was no way in hell that I was letting these dudes hold my belongings. I still didn't trust them enough.

"Ah, she's uptight. It's okay. We understand," Fola rebounded. "She's a smart one."

"What I really want to do is smoke a joint. Since you know your way around here, I'm sure you could point me to a few good shops."

As we walked, I heard a multitude of English-speaking dialects, and there were American flags planted here and there. Fola explained to me that several expats set up shop here since so many people spoke English in Amsterdam. I could even decipher the Dutch that was being spoken in some of the shops. So it wasn't a far stretch that some American kids would get caught up in the freely flowing drugs and sex that pervaded this city. The effects of excess surrounded us. I saw ragged college kids, swathed in blankets, sitting on the streets, wasted, with no way of getting home. These kids had smoked, snorted, or injected their school tuition away, and were out of options. Some girls resorted to prostitution, but the competition was stiff. Mainly, the club kids scavenged for money, partied, and found some place to crash in the early dawn. It was a sad sight to see, and I knew that I didn't want to get caught up. Celé knew all the spots to get the best drugs, but Fola seemed more reserved.

We strolled along the cobbled streets gawking at the coke-heads, sexpots, and potheads who filled the streets among the drab, faceless tourists. The red-light district appeared tame and nondescript in the afternoon daylight, and I actually found the old, Dutch village quite charming.

"I'd love to have one of those brownies." I pointed to the window display of a small coffee shop along the row of stores. It was the only shop with an American flag, and like the typical tourist who only gravitates toward familiar things in a foreign place I managed to pick out the one American coffee shop in Amsterdam.

"Ah, I see. You want to go to a coffee shop." He gestured his fingers in a bunny ears motion when he said the word coffee. Inside, I asked the clerk for the menu, and he whipped out an extensive laminated sheet of maybe a hundred different types of hash. I knew I could find pot in Amsterdam—that was why so many college kids went there in the first place—I just didn't think the use of the drug would be so open.

"I was looking for the brownies, actually." The clerk handed over a minuscule brown hockey puck-looking brownie, and I was immediately underwhelmed.

"Well, go on and taste it," Fola urged. I took a bite, and all I could taste was chocolate cake. It was delicious chocolate but I couldn't taste any weed. No trace whatsoever. I frowned.

"What's wrong?"

"I don't taste anything. I mean, there's a brownie there, but that's it! I want my money back." Fola and Celé laughed. Even after twenty minutes I didn't feel high in the slightest. Fola seemed to get a kick out of watching me try to get buzzed, and I gathered that he was afraid of being caught with any kind of contraband. He was, after all, a Nigerian citizen, and any infraction would send him back to his home country for good. Celé, I learned, had snuck into Amsterdam via Berlin via Lagos, and therefore could never leave. He lived his life under the radar, and smoked, drank, and snorted his cocaine- and sex-filled nights away when he wasn't working.

"Well, we can always find something better," Fola quipped. Hungrily in search of a buzz, we found another coffee shop offering so many varieties of hash that I needed to sit on a stool to read through the menu. After sorting through the dizzying array of options, I finally selected one that sounded amusing, and possibly strong. I pointed to the selected item on the menu, and the bartender happily supplied a square-shaped miniature bag with the requested drug. He also provided me with a complimentary set of wrapping papers, to which he demonstrated a sophisticated way of wrapping a joint. He folded the rectangular strip into a wide V shape, placed a few crushed leaves inside, and rolled it effortlessly. He licked the seam and stuck the entire joint in his mouth to seal the entire piece. He finished by igniting a lighter across the length of the piece. I tried to do the same but ended up with a crumpled piece of paper, and weed leaves in my lap. A rookie roller. I was happy to smoke a joint and pass it along, but I saved the rolling for the experts. My joints always came out fat at one end and weedless at the other.

We walked around the village, weaving in and out of smoke shops. Fola was intent on watching me get high, so that he could live vicariously through me and avoid extradition. He wasn't taking any chances. We found a small boutique selling all kinds of smoking paraphernalia and went in.

"Have you ever had a shroom?" Celé asked with the excitement of a teenage boy. I shook my head.

"The idea of tripping on something and not having a firm grasp of my surroundings does not appeal to me in the least."
He laughed. "Me neither. Let's try it together!" We purchased the shriveled mushroom and vowed to share it later that evening.
Fola laughed at us in the background, vicariously participating in our drug experimentation. After a while, the effects of the marijuana unexpectedly began to take it's toll and soon I was craving for a more substantive meal to fill my empty stomach. We stopped by a snack shop offering a wrapped piece of parchment filled with thick, piping hot, crispy fries and doused them with ketchup and hollandaise sauce.

Happy and high, Fola, Celé, and I skipped through the streets of Amsterdam, looking at all the raggedy whores lining the windows of the red-light district. It was a sad sight, these women, whose youth had quickly diminished as a result of the rough years in the sex industry. Some women called out from their windows, sweetly luring in potential customers, while others stood in their doorways, smoking cigarettes, in their skimpy, fading lingerie.

"Is this as good as it gets?" I asked. I always had the impression that the red-light district had amazing women coming out of every corner." Fola laughed.

"It's still light out. The good hookers come out at night. You'll see. How are you feeling now?" he asked. "Would you like to put your bags down and relax?" I knew the time would come when I would need to choose whether to stay with my new Nigerian friends, who were still, in effect, strangers, or bail somehow and never speak to them again. Against my better judgment, I decided to go with them, and I thanked God for all my wonderful experiences in life thus far, just in case things went south and I didn't manage to make it to the next day.

"We'll drop off our things and then go get something to eat. There's a great little supper club in the area where we're staying while we're here. The house is about five stops away on the local train." We headed back to Centrale Station and took the metro to Gein, a suburb outside Amsterdam. The area where they stayed was not very different from the Marcy Projects in Brooklyn, or the neglected tenements in south Philadelphia or Pittsburg, Pennsylvania. These projects were low-lying and painted a homely shade of blue. Outside, several lines of clothing hung from the upper-level apartments, and I could hear children running and playing in the area, despite the desolate courtyard.

Fola rang the doorbell and we were buzzed into the complex. An older Nigerian woman, casually dressed in a velour tracksuit, greeted us at the apartment door. She put me somewhat at ease, and she gave off a motherly vibe. She greeted Fola and Celé with a hug and waved us in. The apartment was tight but cozy. We passed the kitchen where the early evening sun streamed inside onto the white tile floors, reflecting off the garish green cabinet treatments. Fola gently rubbed my back.

"I know you're tired. You can rest for a bit before we go out. Or we can just go out now and then you can rest before we go to the clubs." I opted to eat first.

"I just want to gather my things and freshen up a bit. Can I have a minute?" Fola directed me to a small bedroom and I closed the door behind me, glad to have some privacy. I sat on the bed strategizing. I knew I wanted to have a good time, but I also wanted to be safe. The presence of the older woman reassured me enough that I decided to stay and see what would unfold in the night. I gathered my passport, travel documents, and other identification and slipped them discreetly under my clothing. Just then Fola knocked.

"Can I come in?"

"Just a second." I took a look in the mirror to make sure I looked inconspicuous, and then hid my bag under the bed. I figured if there was going to be any attempt at rape or murder, I would at least have a way to get back home once I escaped. I opened the door. Fola had changed into a thin black tee that accented his muscular frame. I had to catch myself as I stared at his dark chocolate body.

"I'm ready." Fola, Celé, and I headed out into the evening to a nearby restaurant for dinner. The owners were busy cooking and preparing for the busy weekend night that was to come. The space was a dining area, which opened up to a larger dance space. Above this space was a large flat-screen TV, where an African man, dressed in a purple pimp suit sang, flanked by dozens of gyrating booties. A few patrons sat at the sparse tables, staring at the screen sipping Guinness.

"Who is that? I asked Fola, pointing to the screen. He laughed, and for the first time, I noticed his startlingly white smile.

"Oh, that's Dr. Sakis. He's really popular, and he has the best dancers." I couldn't help think of Luke and 2Live Crew, the images of oiled asses in G-strings dancing to the thumping Miami bass. Only the Dr. Sakis girls shook with more conviction. I was fixated on these girls as they so effortlessly jiggled their asses to the beat. Celé tapped me. He had an ice-cold Heineken in hand.

"Thirsty? I took the bottle and sat down at a table while Fola and Celé conversed with the restaurant owner in their native dialect. So far the night had been good for me. Out of all the opportunities these guys had to commit a crime, they had taken no liberties. Maybe they were okay after all. I ordered a plate of fried fish and plantains while the guys ordered a thick stew with a side of fufu, a floured dough ball. We devised a plan for the evening.

"So what did you want to do?" Fola asked me.

"Well, I'd like to go to the red-light district and see the real action. I feel like I only got a taste. Let's go down there and see what happens."

"Do you want to shower and rest first?" Celé asked. "You've been going nonstop since the morning!" I thought about it and realized that I did need a rest. My emotions were still in Paris with all of the drama with Tristan and Emiline, and with being accosted by the French equivalent of the FBI I was a little overwhelmed.

"Yeah, I think I'll take a nap before we go out." We went back to the apartment, and I fell asleep, with my valuables tucked tightly under my body.

~

I awoke to the sound of raucous laughter outside the door. I didn't anticipate guests and was completely disheveled and caught off-guard. There was a knock on the door.

"Sleeping beauty. Are you awake?" It was Fola. I opened the door.

"What time is it?"

"It's a little after ten. Do you want to start getting ready?"

"For sure. What's going on outside?"

"Oh, just some friends having a few drinks and watching a movie. Come and introduce yourself if you want." The crowd in the living room was a welcome mix of men and women that put me at ease. I waved quickly and got a rousing hello in return. I finally got dressed, slipping on a fuchsia Sonia Rykiel tank, black stretch miniskirt, and booties. I was ready for the night.

~

I'm not sure what I was expecting walking along the cobbled streets surrounding the canals. I anticipated an all-out sexfest but what I saw were hordes of crowds seeping through dark red-hued alleyways. Fola, Celé, and I ducked in and out of back alleys, peering at the prostitutes that lined their red-lit entryways. We gawked and compared, laughed, and scoffed at the selection. At one point Celé parted from our pack in search of some weed, and Fola and I were left alone to explore. Fola grabbed my hand.

"So what should we do?" I gazed around at the plethora of sex-toy shops and peep shows.

"Well, I've never been to a peep show."

"Okay, then let's go!" We stopped in front of a venue advertising one-euro peep shows, and went inside. There were several booths aligned in a circle surrounding the main stage. We sat in one of the booths, inserted the coin, and waited for the show to start.

The black booth was suddenly illuminated and a red, velvet curtain opened in front of the glass window to reveal the performers. The woman was tall and stunning, likely of Eastern European origin. Her cropped brunette hair accentuated her flawless face and full lips. Her companion was equally stunning, impeccably built, with strong, muscular arms and legs, and a boy-ish, brown crew cut that outlined his chiseled face. We watched as the male grabbed her tiny waist, sucking on her small round breasts. Her long legs were accentuated by her glittering platform heels and she wrapped them around his torso. The man in turn spun her lithe body around and licked her ass, and she moaned. His cock was enormous, hanging long and viciously from his body, but she handled it easily, taking the entire member into her mouth and deep-throating him. I could feel Fola's breath getting heavier, and the sexual anticipation filled the booth. He leaned into my ear and kissed the lobe while simultaneously adding another coin to the pay slot to keep the show going.

"Do you like that?" he asked. I laughed suggestively, and just as I leaned in for a kiss, the lights came on.

"What the hell? I thought we got more time than that!" I shouted, exasperated. The performers paused mid-act, staring down at one corner booth. Apparently the customer did not pay his share so the show was over for everybody. The performers asked him to leave and he agreed, and the show resumed. No more than a few minutes later, they stopped again, this time infuriated with the non-paying customer. After first leaving, he managed to make his way back into another booth, but again refused to pay. The male performer, now standing and holding his lover upside down with his head buried in her pussy, cartwheeled the woman down and proceeded to curse the cheapskate out. This show was over and I was annoyed.

"I didn't even get to see them fuck!"

Fola laughed quietly and kissed me softly on the cheek. "There are others, don't worry." We left the peep show and Celé called Fola to inform him that he had found a most excellent selection of weed and would be enjoying it in a quiet corner of a canal.

The night was perfect. It was late August and the summer heat was light and welcoming. An excited buzz filled the air as would-be patrons eagerly traversed the cobbled streets looking for the perfect means to fulfill their sexual desires. I turned to Fola.

"Have you ever had sex with one of these women in here?"

"No," he answered flatly. "I honestly never had the interest to even try." I looked at him sideways. He shrugged incredulously. "Seriously! Look, if you want to try it, we can go in together." I hadn't contemplated actually having sex with a hooker in Amsterdam. The last time I fucked a woman was back in college, when I was feeling a bit experimental.

Fola looked at me deeply. "Have you ever had sex with a woman?" I was taken aback by the question. It was as if he had been reading my mind.

Masha. She was Eastern European, with disheveled, dirty-blond hair that formed soft ringlets around her delicate face. She was a Fine Arts major, with a concentration in painting and often appeared covered in chalk or acrylic paint. I wasn't so much attracted to her body as to her intellect, which fascinated and confused me all at once. We would converse for hours while we worked, and I fell in love with her full lips and supple breasts that hung freely beneath her thin tank tops.

Sometimes we would study late at night in the lower level of the NYU library, where they allowed students to stay overnight to work. We usually went earlier in the evening so that we could snag one of the private, soundproof study rooms. It must have been finals when Masha and I were doing one of our late-night study gigs writing essays on Kant's philosophical theories. She said something smart and funny, and I laughed and leaned over to kiss her on the lips. Unplanned and unexpected, we were both taken by surprise. She returned my advance with a deep kiss and I reached to caress her nipples, which poked out of her thin top. She was aroused and moaned in pleasure as she moved closer to me to run her fingers along the outline of my body. I reached down into her paint-splattered shorts and felt past her panties and soft bush until I felt her warm knot on my fingertips. I tickled her clit and she kissed me deeply. Someone dropped a stack of books just outside the door and Masha started, unnerved by the disruption. We laughed at our nervousness and continued, kissing and nibbling each other until we both lay naked on the study table. Her body was youthful and sexy, and as I hovered over her I gazed at her body longingly, stroking my fingers over her soft, milky body. She giggled her smart, confident laugh and I lowered myself to lick her nipples, gently exploring her body until my tongue found its way between her legs.

The inexperience of giving pleasure to a woman halted me a bit as I sucked and nibbled on her moist labia. I knew what I liked as a woman, and going off of this firsthand knowledge, I pleasured her the way I enjoyed being pleasured so many times before. Her body writhed in approval as I continued kissing her, swiftly flicking my tongue over her clit like a soft feather, intensify-

ing my stroke as her body dictated. Her moans became louder, and her body began to tremble before a stream of clear cum trickled out of her pussy onto the tabletop.

"What are you thinking about?" Fola asked me. I had been licking my lips at the thought of the memory.

"Oh nothing," I laughed. Fola leaned down to kiss me, this time more passionately on the lips.

"Does the thought of nothing always make you lick your lips like that?" he asked.

I giggled. "Is it a crime to be in a good mood?" We both laughed.

"So tell me then, have you ever had sex with a woman?"

"What? No. No! I've never done it. Why do you ask?"

"Oh just curious. I mean, we're here in Amsterdam. What better place to experiment?"

"So what do you suggest?" I asked. I knew that he wanted to go inside one of the hooker's dens. I knew he was eager to try and wanted to use me as the conduit for his experimentation.

"Let's pick a girl and go inside. Just to see. We don't have to do anything."

"Yeah, but we'll have to pay either way."

"Well, at least we can always say that we went in. Let's give it a try." We walked up and down the red-lit canals in search of the perfect girl. There were all types—white, black, Asian, dominatrix, and twins. Transsexuals flashed a little cock when we passed their doors. Among the hoards of European thrill-seekers and American college frat boys, I noticed an imposing African man walking alone along the corridors of a canal. His features were strong and handsome, and he walked with a certain confidence that made him stand out, even though his dark skin made him more of a shadow. We passed him and waved in recognition; we must have been the only black people in the street that night, as far as we could tell. As he walked passed, I turned around and glanced toward him, and he did the same.

"Hi," I waved.

"Hello." He spoke with a faint accent infused with years of European influence. "I'm Djeneba. What's up?" I introduced myself and told him I was American. Fola introduced himself as well, with a tinge of jealousy in his voice. I was happy to tease him by flirting with the man.

"We're just strolling around looking for some fun times. I'm visiting from America via Paris. Where are you from?"

"I'm from Mali. I'm just in town for some business meetings. Is this your first time in Amsterdam?"

"I've been here several times," Fola chimed in, not to be excluded from the conversation. "I'm just introducing my girl to the place."

I was a bit taken aback by his use of the possessive term "my girl." I was sexually attracted to him, but I honestly didn't think that this adventure would develop into a relationship. I was just there to enjoy myself as an independent woman.

"This place seems like a playground for men. Where are all

the hot guys for us single chicks?"

"You can find them if you look around. They are here. But I don't know how your guy would feel about that." I laughed flirtatiously. "I'm sure he wouldn't mind watching." We all laughed.

"I never tried any of these girls here. They're not my type," Fola added with bravado.

"Oh yeah, bro? So what the hell are you doing in Amsterdam?" the Malian man asked suspiciously.

"The same thing as you, bro. Just cruising the streets."

"Ah, there's a nice one." The Malian man pointed to a petite Taiwanese hooker dressed in a schoolgirl uniform, complete with white thigh-highs, pigtails, and a pair of thick black-frame glasses. Her baby face was masked partially by the red light that hung above her door.

"Hi there," she beckoned, and he smiled eagerly.

"Ah, I see you like them on the small side," I commented.

"Yeah, easier to throw around," he laughed. "I think I might take her. The girl next door is not bad either. You should go." Fola and I looked at each other. "Let's go," I said, grabbing his hand. I had no intentions of having sex, but I did want to go inside.

"Konnichiwa," the Japanese whore cooed. She was a cute girl, petite with a curvaceous frame. She wore a white latex bikini and thigh-high boots that reflected the soft red glow of her red-lit room. "Come inside." I couldn't help thinking that was a metaphor for all her johns as I entered her den.

The room was a sparse square, likely painted white, but colored a hazy red from the florescent bulb that hung above us. The bed sat in the middle of the room, and in a corner was a short bar stool. The perimeter of the room was decorated with plush animals in various neon hues. A small table beside the bed held a glass bowl of condoms decorated with anime characters, and a roll of paper towels. I addressed the hooker.

"Listen. I don't want to have sex. We can just chat, if you want. Really. It's more for the experience." Fola laughed hysterically. "Are you serious?" he asked, flabbergasted.

"Yes, I'm serious, Fola. Let's just chill." I knew I was being a total cock tease, having a man sit in a room with a cute Japanese hooker and me, without having sex. I could only imagine the thoughts of a three-way tryst circling inside his head. "You can tell all your friends whatever you want about the experience." I turned my focus on the girl, who had moved to a stool in the corner, bemused at the quarreling couple.

"You know there is still a fee even if there is no sex?" she asked.

"Of course. I just wanted see what it was like inside. But can I ask you something? What is the craziest thing you have done on the job?" Just as she was about to answer, I heard the faint sound of a kitten meowing.

"Did you hear that?" I asked.

"I don't hear anything, except a bunch of crazy people outside," Fola responded.

"Shhh. Listen." I could hear the kitten again.

"I hear it!" Fola and the hooker exclaimed. The woman searched under the bed for the critter, while we looked around the tiny room.

"There's really nowhere for the kitten to go, as you can see," she stated, matter-of-factly. I got an idea and hopped on the bed to put my ears to the wall. Fola followed, and we both busted out laughing. Through the walls we could hear the sound of that sweet-looking Taiwanese hooker in the schoolgirl outfit getting her back blown out by the hulking Malian man we met on the street. We heard the slap of flesh hitting flesh, as the poor girl let out a yelp that sounded like a helpless kitten with every thrust. We all collapsed on the bed in uncontrollable laughter.

"Okay. Let's go. What do we owe you?" I asked.

"Eh, it's on the house. Thanks for giving me some comedy for the night." I left her a few bills in her Hello Kitty tip jar, and we headed back out to the street. As if on cue, Celé called to tell us that he was finished with the weed and needed something else to do.

"Let's go to a club," I volunteered. "Are there any clubs that don't blast techno music all night?"

"I know this club not too far from here that plays a lot of hip-hop, if that's what you want," Fola suggested. "We can take a taxi there." I was relieved at the sound of the words hip-hop. Since coming to Paris, I had been submerged in an endless rut of Europop, cheap rap, and American megahits. I just wanted to hear some raw lyricism instead of the mind-numbing thump I heard daily in the Paris shops and streets.

We arrived at the club, and the heavy bass of a classic Biggie joint poured out of its doors as a few revelers entered and exited the building. The club stood in a desolate strip of town surrounded only by a few empty corporate buildings and a twenty-four-hour mart. But somehow I felt incredibly safe in the outskirts of this Dutch town. We went inside and Fola bought me a cocktail as I surveyed the room, filled wall to wall with Africans living in Europe. I could always observe the distinction between a black American traveler and an African traveler. For me, the traveling Africans carried a certain international swag that could be detected almost immediately in their clothing, their speech, and their stance, while they effortlessly held conversations in several different languages.

A Buju Banton song came on and my hips instantly responded to the music. I handed my drink and my jacket to Fola and glided to the center of the dance floor where I was sure to get attention. I had no problem wining to the bump riddim beat in plain view, knowing I would catch the eyes of all the men and women in the room. A man approached me from behind and began grinding against my backside while he groped my waist. He said nothing, and let the music guide our movements. I could sense everyone watching us, our sensual movements creating a sexual heat that permeated the room. I closed my eyes, taking in the deep strum of the bass and the faint, but familiar smell of Senegalese incense.

"Did you forget about your drink?" Fola's voice jarred me

from my reggae trance. I looked up to see him standing in front of me, his eyes dark with lust and envy at the man who had been occupying the space behind me.

"Oh thanks," I replied. "I am a little thirsty." I took a sip. It was my favorite standby, an amaretto sour. "Would you like to dance with me?"

"I'm not much of a dancer. I don't mind watching you though. I'm going to sit over there in the corner with Celé."
I felt bad. Fola had invited me out and here I was dancing with every man but him in the club. I went and sat with him and Celé.

"So how do you guys know about this club?"

"We've been going here for a while now. It's the only place that plays the music we really want to hear. Everywhere else is techno music." I could relate to their sentiment. "Well, thanks for taking me out. I was getting a little tired of the Euro music, too." I stood and grabbed Fola's hand. "Come dance with me." He cowered. "I promise to guide you. Don't be scared."

"Okay, but only in the corner. I don't want to make a fool of myself." I led him to a dark corner of the club where a few patrons were sipping Heinekens and discreetly smoking weed. Pressing him against the wall, I grinded my hips against his, gently rotating my body so that he would follow suit.

"Just do what my body does. It's easy," I whispered in his ear. I could feel his pants stiffen and he became aroused. "You see? You're a pro!" I laughed seductively. Just then, the DJ switched the song to a popular hip-hop song and the crowd was jumping again. I left Fola standing there, on the dance floor.

~

It may have been four or five in the morning when we returned to the house. Everyone else was sleeping and we tiptoed into our rooms. I wasn't exactly keen on having sex with Fola. For one, I was exhausted—I had had a long day of travel and excitement, and I just wanted to sleep at that point. I also couldn't stop thinking about Tristan in Paris, dog that he was.

"Listen Fola, I'm really tired okay. Let's just go to sleep." "That's okay, darling. I know. Can we talk for a while? I promise I won't touch." I laughed. "Okay, if you promise to behave. But don't be offended if I fall asleep between words." We both laughed and he left me to change my clothes for bed. When I was tucked in, he knocked on the door, and I let him come in and lie down next to me. We both stared at the ceiling, but I honestly didn't feel a drop of sexual tension. Just as I was about to drift to sleep, Fola broke our silence.

"I'm so glad you came. I didn't think you would actually come, you know?"

"Yeah, you took a big risk, sending me that money for the ticket I mean, we only just met on the plane to Paris!"

"Yes, but something about you told me that I could trust you. Can I ask you something?

"Sure."

"Can I kiss you?" I sighed deeply. Here we go, I thought. I would have to push this man off or run away in the middle of the night.

"Just on the cheek. I promise I won't go further. Unless you ask me to."

"Okay, I will take a kiss on the cheek, but then it's bedtime." He kissed me soft and tenderly, and sat back to gauge my response. I closed my eyes and feigned sleep.

"Can I ask you something else?" Fola hesitantly asked. I sighed. "Go ahead," I replied. He breathed in deeply. "Can I kiss your pussy?" he asked, earnestly. I gagged.

"What?" I laughed, incredulously.

"Please? It would be such an honor." I busted out laughing.

"No, you cannot kiss my pussy. I'm going to sleep now." He was silent for a minute.

"Please?"

"No!" I turned over in the bed.

"But why can't you just give me a chance? I promise I won't disappoint you."

"I'm not interested, but thanks for the offer. Now can I go to sleep?" I was exasperated.

"Okay, I know you're tired," Fola responded, dejected.

"Thank you." I felt my eyes getting heavier with the onslaught of sweet slumber not too far behind. Fola lay still beside me.

"Is it me? Am I not attractive? I thought we had a connection!" I sighed deeply into my pillow. "Can we just talk about this tomorrow? I just want to get like, at least two hours of sleep. I have been going nonstop since this morning. I am exhausted."

"I know, I know, but this question keeps ringing in my mind. I am crazy about you." I ignored his statement. He nudged me. "Did you hear me?" I feigned sleep. He nudged me again.

"What is it?" I angrily whispered.

"I asked you a question."

"Look, I'm not having sex with you. I'm not doing anything sexual with you. I am tired. I'm not interested. Please let me sleep." If that statement wasn't finite enough, then I didn't know what else I could say. I curled back under the covers and tried to go to sleep.

"But you haven't told me exactly why?" Damn, this guy was persistent. I knew that I wasn't going to get any sleep as long as I lay beside him. I took my pillow and a blanket and walked out of the bedroom to the living room. I would have to sleep on the couch.

~

"French toast?" I awoke to a smiling Nigerian man standing over me wearing a brightly-colored apron and wielding a spatula. The blazing morning sun was streaming throughout the house, adding to the man's cheerful demeanor. I laughed.

"Um, sure, I would love some French toast." Just then Fola walked into the living room. He smiled at me.

"Oh, this is Tammi. He's the man of the house," Fola laughed, making air quotes. Tammi. The irony of the homemaking man's name made me giggle. "His wife is the lady you met at the door last night. She's still sleeping."

"I need a husband like him," I laughed, pointing to Tammi.

"You never know. The man of your dreams might be right in front of your eyes," the man replied.

"So, how is my sleeping beauty this morning?" Fola asked. I couldn't help but smile at his upbeat disposition, despite our less than friendly early-morning encounter.

"I'm better. A little more rested. How are you?"

"Me, I feel great!" I could tell he had already showered and dressed. "So, what would you like to do today?" Luckily for me I had researched some fun things to do in Amsterdam before I left Paris, so I had a loose itinerary of the best way to enjoy my brief stay.

"Well, I thought we could go to the van Gogh Museum and then visit a few art galleries along the canal. Maybe some lunch. Just explore the city, you know?"

"That sounds great. It will be just you and me. Celé has some things to do in another town. So we'll have no distractions." After the events of the early morning, I knew I was in for a lot of sexual pressure from this man, but figured I would play along. I was, after all, his guest, and since I had arrived in Amsterdam, I hadn't laid out a single euro.

"So once you've had breakfast, we can get ready to go. It's your day."

~

We took the train back down to Centrale Station where we could easily walk around the canals and view the shops. I saw some familiar American stores like H&M and Levi's as well as a slew of funky clothing and shoe shops. I ventured into a shop covered wall-to-wall with exotic shoes and boots of all shapes and colors. I had no money for shopping, but I figured I would enjoy myself anyway. I spotted a pair of leather, punkish booties in an off-white shade.

"You should try them on," Fola cajoled. I asked a saleswoman for my size and she brought out the boots along with a few other suggestions. The supple leather felt like butter in my fingertips, and I slid them over my bare feet before walking around the store in them.

"These are pretty awesome."

"Do you want them?"

"Oh no, I don't have a budget for shopping. I'm just playing dress-up."

"But if you like them, I will get them for you."

"Are you serious? No, I couldn't. I don't even know how much they are." As I reached down to get a look at the price on the box, Fola snatched it away.

"Excuse me, miss." He summoned the saleswoman. "We'd like these."I blushed at his brazenness. I never had a man splurge on me like that, and I felt a hot flush come across my face as I tried to hide my excitement and embarrassment over Fola's behavior in that instant. I was never one to be a gold digger, but I was also smart enough to take up a good opportunity. Suddenly, I thought of all the things I wanted to buy, but couldn't afford at the moment. A Louis Vuitton bag? An Hermès scarf? A Fendi miniskirt? How far could I push my luck, I wondered.

"There is this fragrance that I have been mesmerized by, ever since it came out. It's called "Paris," by Yves Saint Laurent. Have you heard of it?"

Fola thought for a moment. "No, I haven't, but I'm sure we can find it in one of these shops." He scanned the store windows, looking for the object of my desire. We ventured into a beauty department store, and Fola left me to play in the lipsticks and blushes. As I swiped a tissue over a tube of Beaujolais lipstick to sample, I overheard Fola behind me, pressing the saleswoman for a bottle of my coveted perfume.

"No, we don't have it in stock right now. It will ship next week."

"But are you sure? I need to have it right now." I could hear the desperation in his voice and ran to him.

"Fola, Fola, it's okay, really. I don't have to have it right now—it's okay. I really appreciate it," I stressed.

"No, no, I must get this perfume for you. Anything for

my girl." *My girl.* There he was, throwing around that possessive phrase. I laughed uneasily.

"I appreciate that, but I'm really here to have a good time. Let's go someplace else." We walked past some studios where painters and sculptors were feverishly working just inside of their large-paned windows. Among these galleries, I spotted a partially hidden antique shop, filled with vintage toys from the early-twentieth century.

"Oh Fola, I have to go inside." The shop owner greeted us as I pored over the delicate china dolls and dusty dollhouse furniture. In a corner of a wooden dresser I spotted a painted brass Popeye and Olive Oil doll set.

"My mother always loved Olive Oil," I sighed.

"How much is it?" Fola asked the shopkeeper. "The doll?"

"Oh Fola, I was just looking," I turned around to say, but by then, he had already purchased the toy and was getting his change.

"Let's have lunch," Fola said, smiling. Fola suggested we grab some traditional Dutch fare, but our shopping forays across town put me in the mood for a juicy grilled steak.

"Are there any steak houses around here?" Realizing how American that sounded, I added, "My energy's a little low. I think I'm lacking some iron." We found what looked like a tribute to Western-style barbeque and settled down. Fola looked deep in my eyes as the waiter placed the menus before us.

"I think I'm in love with you." I laughed at him.

"Love? How can you be in love with me? We barely even know each other!"

"Rome wasn't built in a day. We can grow to love each other."

"You're getting ahead of yourself. Look, I am really enjoying this time I'm with you. It's a great experience for me. But as for romance, why don't we just take it easy and see where things lead us?"

I was cherishing the time I was having with Fola, but the truth of the matter was that my heart was still with Tristan, and no matter how hard I tried to erase him from my mind and revel in the moment, I just couldn't seem to get him out of my mind. And when I wasn't thinking about Tristan, I was thinking about Abdoulaye back in New York. Who knew whom he was likely fucking when I wasn't there. This revelation shocked me for a moment. I had always envisioned myself as a free-thinking, open-relationship type of person, too independent to be tied down to the confines of a traditional relationship. Jealousy was just not the emotion that so-called progressive, open-minded women like me felt. So why would I care that these males with whom I had become intimate were openly engaged in sexual relationships with other women? I was angry and appalled at myself. Not only for allowing myself to become involved in these hopeless love triangles but also for the fact that I had a caring gentleman doting on me hand and foot, and I cared nothing for him.

"What are you thinking?" Fola's masculine voice broke my train of thought.

"I'm just enjoying the moment."

"By the looks on your face, I wouldn't gather so. You look quite perplexed."

"Oh, don't worry. I'm always making faces and I don't even know it. I'm having a great time." Fola grabbed my hand.

"I'll do anything to make you happy."

~

After a day of shopping, gallery and museum hopping, and strolling through the city, I was ready to go back to the apartment for a catnap. I had to have enough energy for the night's debauchery if there was any to be had. Given the circumstances, I had grown to feel safe and secure in the hands of Fola. I hadn't been kidnapped, raped, or murdered at this point, and I figured there had been enough witnesses if there were any shady business going down. I lay my head on the welcoming bed and fell into a soft slumber. Fola was nowhere to be found.

~

I awoke to darkness and a still house. What the hell had I done? Maybe it was a setup after all, and the Nigerians had buttered me up with gifts and entertainment to throw me off-guard so that they could assassinate me and steal my documents. I felt underneath my tank top where I had been keeping my passport and other travel documents in a plastic pouch underneath my bra. Seeing that they were still there, I took a deep breath and slowly moved out of my bed.

"Sleeping beauty? Are you awake?" My heart jumped a little bit. Fola knocked and came into the room slowly.

"Can you turn on the light please?" He did and laughed quietly to himself. I realized that I might have looked a bit disheveled sitting in the middle of the bed, cross-legged in my pink tracksuit—less like an independent woman, and more like a pet rabbit who had lost its way. "What?" I asked.

"You just look so confused, like a little puppy. I just want to take care of you."

"Thanks, but I'm fully capable of taking care of myself," I rebuffed. Fola moved closer to me and sat on the bed.

"May I kiss you?"

"Fola, not this again." He leaned in to kiss me on the lips and I turned my head at just the right time so that his lips grazed my cheek.

"Why are you playing so hard to get?"

"I'm not. This is how I really feel. Look, I'm still technically in a relationship with my guy in Paris. I'm really not trying to be in another situation right now." Fola huffed at my statement. "Forget about that guy. He's a loser. What is it about him? What does he do for you?"

I admittedly couldn't answer the question. What, exactly, had Tristan done for me that had made him seem like such an amazing guy? I mean, the dude was playing me and I was sucking up his behavior like a helpless lap dog.

"I know what it is. You American girls are attracted to these French guys, because you love the romance of it. Like in the movies." He was right. Part of me really wanted my relationship with Tristan to work because I wanted to live the fantasy that I had seen so many times on TV and in the movies. But another part of me cherished the little things that Tristan had opened me up to—a world of jazz, poetry, and art that I had never known or thought to explore.

Since being in Paris, I had grown a small repertoire of music that enhanced my experience and made me feel fuller, rounder—like a mature woman. I was listening to John Coltrane and Louis Armstrong, Salif Keita and Sei Ragi Khan, like I had never known them before. My days would start with a buttered baguette, a cup of tea, and the sound of Ella Fitzgerald cooing alongside Louis Armstrong as I read the morning news and gazed out of Tristan's third-story apartment overlooking a quiet street. I found romance in staring out across the alleyway at the neighbor washing and hanging her laundry and tending to her ivy and flowers that hung colorfully outside her windowsill. It was more than Tristan whom I was in love with. I was in love with Paris.

"Do you want to go out now?" he asked.

"Sure, but where is everybody?"

"Oh, they all left. It is a Saturday night, you know. Tammi's wife is still here, sleeping. She went to bed early so that she could go to church in the morning." The thought of the older woman in the house reassured me.

"Okay, let me take a quick shower and throw something on. Did you have something particular in mind?"

"I figured we could just walk around. Talk. Smoke weed." I laughed at the thought of Fola attempting to roll a joint and smoke it. I doubt he even knew how to pull the seeds from the bundle of herbs.

"Maybe we can find some good hash tonight," I laughed.

"Maybe I can get lucky tonight," Fola laughed.

~

We strolled the red-light district once again, ignoring the gaudy whores who seemed to dangle out of every corner with comedic enthusiasm. As I walked, staring at the garish lights, I could feel Fola's eyes gazing at my body. I had chosen to wear a pair of black leggings, my new booties he had purchased for me earlier that day, and my pink Sonia Rykiel tank top, covered with my cropped black leather jacket. I felt a little punkish, a little Euro, and totally sexy.

"That was crazy, what happened last night with that Malian guy!" I quipped.

"I saw the way you were looking at him. You liked him."

"What? You're crazy."

"If you had the choice, would you rather fuck him or me?"

"Neither. I want my Parisian boyfriend," I teased. Fola sighed and pulled me close to kiss me fully on the lips. I let myself go and fell into the passion of the moment, allowing my body to fall deeply into his as he fully engulfed my lips in his mouth. An un-expected fire rose through my body as I felt his broad hands glide from the center of my back, down to my ass, where he squeezed and caressed both cheeks with his broad hands. He sucked on my bottom lip for a moment before releasing it to look deeply into my eyes.

"I have to have you," he moaned. I laughed at his intent. "Well, before you take me, can we find some good weed to smoke first? I would hate to leave Amsterdam without getting a good drag!" Just then a disheveled man approached us with what looked like an ounce of pure hash.

"I'll give you a good price for it." Fola took a long hard look at the bag, which looked like a huge ball of lint. I did't think he would know a good bag of weed if he were sitting on a weed farm in Cartagena.

"Nah, we won't take it. Thanks for the offer anyway."

"Fola, you didn't even smell it to see if it was legit."

"Did you see that guy? Would you buy ANYTHING from that guy?" We both laughed at the absurd notion.

"Let's go to this place." I pointed to a darkly lit café with a few patrons inside playing pool. "This seems low-key enough. I just want a quiet place to smoke for a bit and just people watch." We walked inside where I proceeded to the bar to order up the best bag of weed that I had ever tasted. I closed my eyes, put my finger on the sticky laminated sheet, and picked a blend.

"Oh, you'll like that one. It's smooth, and finishes off softly. Enjoy it," the shopkeeper laughed.

Fola and I sat down in a corner, and he watched me as I opened the little baggie, pulled apart the bush of herbs, carefully picking out the seeds, and carefully setting it aside so that I could slice my Dutchmaster.

"You're awfully good at that." He watched as I cut the fat cigar down the center lengthwise and emptied its contents onto the side of the table. I slid the tobacco paper in my mouth, flattening it, and carefully laid the herbs inside before rolling it and sealing it with a lighter.

"Actually not. I have never rolled an expert joint. I'm still a rookie actually."

"I wouldn't know it." He smiled at me adoringly. I handed him my digital camera.

"Take my picture." I lit my joint and blew a perfect smoke ring from my lips as he snapped away. I stopped smoking to take a look at the results. I saw multiples of me in the same frame covered in various shades of red and magenta from the fluorescent lights on the street. It was as if I were in some sort of a trippy, watercolor haze, engulfed in a haze of smoke. "I love this."

"I could take your picture all day." He reached over to stroke my cheek with his finger.

"Fola, I can't tell you how much I appreciate everything

you've done for me this weekend. I really needed this excursion."

"I will do anything to win your heart. Anything." He reached into his coat pocket and pulled out a small pink box. It was the Yves Saint Laurent Paris fragrance that I wanted. I gasped. "Fola! You got it! But I thought it was sold out everywhere. How did you find it?"

"I told you, I would do anything for you. I will search high and low for anything that makes you happy." I nearly cried when he said this. Why was it that as women we always fell for the ass-holes, but the men who poured out their entire hearts and souls to us were constantly rejected by us? No wonder so many of us were lonely, single, and bitter.

"Fola. You are a great guy. My head is just not in the right place right now. I'm not asking you to wait for me, but maybe we should come together at another time and place when I am free to give myself to you fully. Right now . . ." my voice trailed off.

"Don't cry babe. I only want you to be happy. Do whatever your heart says. Do you want to leave now?"

"Yeah. Let's just walk in silence okay? Enjoy the city and just listen to its sounds."

"I'm down with that." Fola grabbed my hand and we walked until the faintest purples grazed the horizon. We stood on a lonely canal looking at the empty town, and Fola whispered in my ear and held me tight. "Let's go home."

~

"Can I please kiss your pussy? Please?" Fola was pleading with me.

"Fola, no. This can't happen right now."

"But why? You can't deny the chemistry between us."

"Fola please."

"I promise you won't regret it." Fola got up from the bed and got on his hands and knees.

"What are you doing? Get up!" I whispered. Fola clasped his hands in prayer form.

"Please, girl, I'm begging you. Please! For the love of God!"

I laughed out loud. He had to be desperate if he was pleading to God for help to fulfill his sexual fantasy. I was conflicted. Fola had been so good to me during my stay in Amsterdam. I knew this man would take care of me for life. But my heart was still set on that bastard Tristan, back in Paris. I knew I had to go back and resolve some issues there, likely resulting in the end of the affair. I hated having to think about the heartbreak that lay ahead.

"Okay, go ahead," I relented. I knew I was attracted to the man, but I tried my best to stifle my desire so that he wouldn't get too excited. He climbed back on the bed and kissed my neck and lips repeatedly until my nipples began to harden.

"Hmm, I can see you're getting excited," Fola beamed. Damn biology.

"Actually, I'm a little cold."

He reached over to the side of the bed, and pulled over a thin white cotton comforter.

"Will this work?" he asked. I nodded, defeated. Fola was on top of me now, softly kissing my lips, chin, and neck. He moved his way down my body, unzipping the hoodie of my Juicy Couture tracksuit and sucking my nipples through my thin T-shirt. I lay deathly still and emotionless as the delicious sensations raged through my body.

My mind was barely present when I finally allowed him to pull down my pants. Luckily the darkness in the room hid my anticipation. I twitched nervously, trying desperately to control my bodily reaction to those fierce sexual sensations, as his lips found his way to the hot zone. He could have kissed me, but he got right down to business. He knew what a girl wanted, but I couldn't let him know that he had won. Instead, I stared at the ceiling, biting my lip to suppress my raging pleasure as this Nigerian hottie lapped his tongue in and out of the deepest recesses of my vagina. After a few minutes he came up from beneath the covers and smiled.

"Am I doing okay?" he asked me, laughing.

"Hmmm", I mustered out of my pursed lips, ambivalently.

"You don't like it?"

"No, I don't," I lied.

"Okay. I will try something else." He dove back down beneath the covers and buried his head deeper into my pussy. I bit my lip hard as Fola did all of his tricks, tossing my clit back and forth between his lips and tongue. He sucked on it for a bit and then pressed the tip of his tongue firmly on my knot, sending a spike of pleasure through my body that made me shudder slightly. If I didn't hold my emotions tight, I was sure to come all over his face.

"Can you please stop?" I asked. He emerged from under the covers.

"Am I doing something wrong?"

"It hurts." Fola laughed. "Girl, stop lying. That does not hurt."

"No, really. I'm really uncomfortable."

"I will rectify that." Under the covers he went to satisfy his seemingly unhappy lady, and I couldn't help but laugh at his voracity. This time he took my entire pussy into his mouth and sucked it gently for a moment before splitting the lips of my labia apart with his tongue. I moaned silently as he spread my thighs high and wide before broadly sweeping his tongue from the bottom of my anus to the top of my mound. He did it again, this time looking directly into my eyes from under the covers to gauge my reaction. I bit my lip and took a deep breath.

"What are you doing?" I asked, rhetorically.

"I'm having a salad." This time I couldn't control my laughter, but before I could utter a word, he drove his tongue deep into my anus, slowly gliding his tongue in and out of the hole. I giggled uncontrollably at this new sensation.

"Okay, can you stop now? Really. Please stop." Fola honored my wishes, and moved beside me to rest.

"Did you enjoy it?

"No, not really."

"There you go, lying again. Why are you such a tease?"

"I'm not trying to be. I told you, I wasn't interested in having sex with you."

"I don't believe that. You may be telling me no, but your body was telling me a different story." He was right. I could deny my attraction until I was blue in the face, but I had absolutely no control over the inevitable biological result of sexual stimulation.

"Okay, well believe what you want. I'm tired, and I don't want to have sex with you." I smiled to soften the blow.

"That's okay. We don't have to have sex . . . now. But it will happen."

"Don't hold your breath."

"I would hold my breath for a lifetime if it meant I would have you in the end." I sighed. Why did this man have to be so damn romantic? I turned to him.

"Can we visit the flower markets tomorrow?"
Fola laughed at my change of subject. "Of course we can. Anything for my love. Anything."

~

The following morning, Fola and I woke up before the rest of the household and went into town for breakfast. I had been hearing about the world-renowned flower markets, and thought it would be a wonderful way to end my trip.

We walked hand in hand along the canals, taking in all the colors of the Bleumenmarkt, the major Dutch flower marketplace. Fola, ever the gentleman, carried my duffel bag as I browsed the stalls and stared in wonderment at the astonishing array of flowers that I longed to take home with me. It was a romantic ending to a sexually charged trip, and though the final result wasn't the climax that Fola had hoped for, he still cherished me nonetheless. We stood in the market among the orange and violet tulips, and varying lengths of ivy, gazing at their beauty.

"You should take home some tulips," Fola suggested, "so that you will remember the sweeter side of Amsterdam."

"I think I'd rather remember the more salacious side," I joked.

"Ah-ha! So you admit you enjoyed my tricks!" Fola explained, referring to his bedroom antics the night before.

"I admit to nothing but enjoying your invitation to this lovely city. Let's meet again okay?" We made our way to Central Station, silent in our reflection of the weekend's events. I didn't know if I would ever actually see Fola again, but deep in my heart, I wanted to rekindle this connection, should my affair with Tristan truly come to an end. We stood on the platform, waiting for my train to Paris. Fola set my bag down and held my face in his broad hands.

"Don't forget me."

~

I came back to Paris, refreshed, determined, and focused to make the most of my trip. My first plan of action was to create an itinerary for my days so that I would be able to learn and see as much of Paris as possible. I would wake up each day, shower and have breakfast, and begin my "workday" at 9 a.m. The workday consisted of reading, writing, researching, and blogging. At noon, I would break for an hour lunch and nap, and then wake up to go out at around 1:30 p.m, so as not to waste the entire day in the house. Tristan was working on a new art project with his stepfather, full-time, so the chances of us seeing each other would greatly be reduced. I cherished those private times apart from him, as it allowed me to truly explore the city, on my own.

I came home one night to the sound of two male voices. Instead of opening the door with my key, I rang the doorbell. Tristan opened and I saw an older gentleman sitting at the kitchen table drinking a glass of red wine.

"This is my father," Tristan said. "We were just having dinner. Would you care to join us?"

"Sure. What are you having?"

"Oh, just a simple quiche Lorraine. We are in a rush, so we don't have time to have a proper dinner. I am helping my dad set up a theater for a new production that is opening in two weeks."

"Sounds exciting," I said, sitting down at the small makeshift table covered with bowls of olives and cheese.

"You know, my father is a painter also. You see that panting on the wall behind you?" I turned around to look. "That's one of his pieces."

"He's into Expressionism, I see." The older man smiled and nodded. He didn't speak much English, and I didn't bother trying to converse with him, using my rudimentary French. Tristan served the dish, and we sat together, quietly, eating. The sound of the forks scraping against the plates with the backdrop of silence was unbearable. The air between Tristan and I hadn't quite cleared since the night he left me alone in his bed before I left for Amsterdam. We had yet to discuss it. It had only been a span of a few days, but it seemed more like an eternity. I took a long gulp of my red wine.

"I'm going to take a bike ride around town. Just to get some fresh air. You two have fun." I grabbed my leather jacket and swiftly headed for the door. "Dinner was great. And nice to meet your dad," I added, halfheartedly.

Tristan waved me off, and I was out, into the night, riding my Velib for the brief twenty minutes the ride allotted, until I needed to swap out another bike for another twenty minutes. It was a crisp August night, still warm, but chilly enough if I had to pedal down a hill. The leather jacket clung to my bare skin, my halter dress blowing in the wind as I pedaled over the Seine. Tonight I would visit the Eiffel Tower, a place that I had visited several times before, but never alone, in the middle of the night. I pedaled through desolate side roads, catching glimpses of the glowing tower, which burst into a dazzling show of sparkling lights every few minutes. I stared at the glittering display, my head cynically cocked to the side.

"Fuck Paris."

It was all a façade, like something in the movies. I wanted to blame my plight on the idea that all French men were assholes, but the truth was that I had gotten myself involved with another emotionally unavailable man. But unlike my African lover back home in New York, I actually felt deeply affected by Tristan's actions. He was someone with whom I thought I might have a future. There was days that I rode around Paris, staring enviously at all the interracial couples, beautiful African women being fawned over by their French partners. I even went so far as to imagine what our child, mine and Tristan's, would look like. I pictured a perky mulatto baby with two cornrows, neatly plaited to frame her round face. Tristan and I would travel the world with her, and she would speak several languages. I played this fantasy in my head, over and over, until it was almost real. What if I got pregnant by this man, right now? I dismissed the irrational thought. We were both essentially poor, suffered a huge language barrier, and of course, the biggest barrier that lay between us—his woman.

I hated being the other woman. Again. For some reason it was easier to swallow the concept with Abdoulaye because I never actually dealt with his other women. I could get a hint of whom they might be, but he was always discreet enough so that none of us would get our feelings bruised too much. And he had the uncanny ability of making me—as well as countless others—feel as if they were singularly the sexiest, most important, and special woman in his life. But Tristan was another experience entirely for me. I was in love and I wanted a future with him that would likely never materialize.

I rode my bike around Paris well into the night, weaving in and out of dark alleyways, watching the nondescript people meander in and out of arched doors. I made my way to the Gare du Nord and watched quietly in a corner as several drug dealers and junkies did their transactions among the glare of the glowing train station. An indescribable funk wafted through the air and the faint smell of butter croissants, salmon, and cat urine filled my nostrils. This was the Paris that no one cared to see. I pedaled home, the wheels of my Velib squeaking against the smooth pavement of the empty Richard Lenoir roadway.

~

Though Tristan and I had barely been talking, we were slowly becoming amicable. He was now working full-time on the theater production with his father, so he had little time to hang around. When he came home, it was usually late, and I was asleep. So I was surprised when he came home early one night and offered to make dinner.

"We haven't spoken for a while. I've been so busy. Please forgive me," he said, quietly. I was taken aback by his apology.

"It's okay, I understand you're busy. I've been keeping busy myself. I have really been getting to know the city. Everyday

I explore another section." Tristan leaned in, fascinated.

"You know, I really admire that about you. Emiline was never like that."

"Like what?"

"She was never the exploring type. I always have to get her to try something new. I think it's amazing how you just take a guidebook and go."

"How is Emiline? I haven't heard or seen from her."

"Oh, she has been studying more frequently and taking more trips for work. She wants to be able to do international flights soon, and the test for that is more extensive."

I nodded, feeling a little better than the woman whom I was competing against for this man's affection. Over the weeks I had been exploring, I had allowed myself to let go and fall deeply into my work so that I would not be completely consumed by romantic thoughts of Tristan. I was happily doing things on my own.

~

Fola had also been calling and e-mailing me, so that was also a welcome diversion. I was still in love with Tristan, but I wasn't reliant on him for his affection anymore. I felt comfortable in my skin the more I had grown accustomed to Parisian life and developed more of my own daily itinerary. It was a typical day when I arrived home from shopping the open-air food markets. I had stopped by a local Monoprix on the way home to pick up my newest indulgence—a fondue cup of rich, dark chocolate pudding. I had just put on a classic Indian album that I had dug up from Tristan's dusty musical archives, and curled up on the couch to enjoy my pudding and a novel when the phone rang.

"Hello?" There was a moment of silence and hesitation before Emiline responded.

"Oh, hello." She sounded less than thrilled, but tried to mask her voice. "So you are still there. How are things?"

"Things are great. Are you looking for Tristan?"

"Yes, I have been trying his cell but I can't seem to reach him."

"Well, he seems to be very busy at the theater with his father."

"The theater?" she asked, confused. She obviously had been completely out of touch with Tristan.

"Yes, they have been working nonstop on the set."

"Would you mind if I stopped by? I wanted to teach you how to make a pear tart. It's very easy."

I had to think about this because I didn't know what kind of relationship she had with Tristan at the moment. For all I knew they could have been together all this time, keeping me in the dark and having secret rendezvous. I knew Emiline was still deeply in love with Tristan and would do anything to have him back including becoming friends with a woman whom she knew was her competition.

"Sure, I guess," I stammered. "It will be something fun to

do while Tristan is out."

~

Emiline took no time in running to the nearest Monoprix and gathering the ingredients that we would need for my culinary lesson. She arrived with bags in hand, and a cheerful grin.

"I thought we could start off with the salmon quiche and then make a simple pear and chocolate tart. It's very, very simple," she assured me as she whizzed through the kitchen, gathering utensils and stirring up a salmon and crème fraiche concoction.

I watched from the sidelines and snapped pictures, haplessly trying to follow the improvised recipe. She popped the quiche in the oven and started working on the pear tart, smearing a healthy amount of Nutella on a prepared crust before adding some canned pears, and covering the pastry with another layer of dough. Soon enough we were sitting down and enjoying the freshly baked goods when we heard the jingle of keys at the door. Tristan walked in and stood dumbfounded at the scene of Emiline and me eating together. He looked at me and then at Emiline.

"Why are you here?" Tristan asked angrily. Emiline blushed, and stood up from the table, stuck for words.

"Emiline was just teaching me how to make a chocolate pear tart." I interjected. "It just came out of the oven. Do you care to try some?" Tristan was staring at Emiline, fuming. I laughed to break the tension, which was thick as the crud at the bottom of the

Seine. "Let's all sit down and have some, shall we?"

"No, thanks. I don't want any," Tristan growled.

"Tristan..." Emiline stammered. Tristan opened his mouth to mutter what I was sure would be a curse, and I jumped to action. I quickly cut a slice of the warm tart, and shoved a piece in Tristan's mouth, and pushed him down onto the couch, playfully. I saw his face lighten as he chewed on the sweet, flaky pastry.

"Not bad," he responded, the tiny flakes of crust spilling from his mouth.

"She's a great teacher. Thanks Emi," I said as I turned to her. She laughed shyly and sat down on the couch. Tristan adjusted his body to move away from her, and I stood between the two of them trying to gauge my next move. The silence was deafening. Looking at Tristan, I noticed a bit of melted chocolate on the corner of his mouth. I bent down in front of him and licked the chocolate off his lip, seductively. He didn't flinch, but Emiline gasped. I giggled and plopped myself down between the two feuding ex-lovers.

"Qu'est-ce-que-tu fait?" Emiline asked incredulously.

"What do you mean? I asked coyly. "We all know why you came here today."

"I . . . I don't know what you're talking about."

"I saw the way you were looking at me when we were in the hammam." I purred.

As Emiline looked at me quizzically, I laughed and playfully poked one of her breasts. Emiline jumped up so fast, she nearly fell to the floor. She looked at both of us in disgust as Tristan laughed uncontrollably.

"Ah, so this is what you like, Tristan?" she asked in French. He became silent, but sat on the couch with a smirk. Emiline continued staring at both of us in disbelief before she finally grabbed her belongings and stormed out of the apartment.
Tristan laughed darkly. "Chienne."

I took that as a compliment.

~

The time Tristan and I spent out of each other's sight actually strengthened the friendship we had, and it always made dinnertime a little easier to digest. Emiline was now a distant memory, but it made no difference. Tristan and I hadn't been intimate since the night he left me alone in his bed, and I had not craved his affection since. Our relationship had become purely platonic. Every day Tristan would bring home a little trinket—a morsel of food to eat, an exotic toy, an interesting book—any little thing to discuss. He knew I was amused by these things, and by the end of my stay I had amassed a small tin box of collectible knickknacks to cherish when I arrived home to Brooklyn.

It was one of my final nights in Paris when Tristan asked me to take a bike ride with him around town. I decided to dress casual chic, just in case we decided to stop by a bar for drinks.

I slipped on a slim pair of dark denim jeans, a pair of black stiletto booties, and a slinky top that I covered with a cropped denim jacket.

"You look hot," Tristan laughed as he glanced over my body, staring at my hips. Though he was flirting with me, I felt no pressure to reciprocate in any way. We were completely at ease with each other.

"I know," I said smirking. "I always like to be prepared."

"Ah, you American girls. Always prepared." I'm going to take my bike. You can use Emiline's if you want. She was never fond of it anyway. I made it especially for her, but I guess it was too sporty for her taste." I stared at the wildly concocted bike, with its randomly-sourced parts, and saw the charm in his creation. The seat was uncomfortably firm, but otherwise sturdy. "I can handle this," I assured him, as we rode out of the alleyway.

We rode our bikes around the seedier parts of Paris, going in and out of narrow streets. We landed on a street lined with prostitutes and Tristan whistled my way to have a look. I looked over at the homely women who looked no better than the whores I had seen prancing down the West Side Highway in New York City in the late '80s. These Parisian hookers were no chicer despite the romanticized depictions in romance novels and movies. We rode our bikes past a club blaring hip-hop music.

"You want to go in?" Tristan asked.

"Why not? I'm curious to see how the Parisians get down to Jay-Z," I laughed.

"Let's ride around the corner and lock our bikes into a station. We'll see if they'll let us in. The door looks pretty tight."(using Tristan's spare bike)

"Is it as bad as the clubs in New York City? Sometimes they make you wait for hours to get in. It's for the cache, to make it seem like the place is more popular than it really is."

"I don't think it's quite that bad. And I would never wait for an hour to get into a club. I'm not really into clubs anyway. I'm just going in for the—how do you say—the experience." I laughed at his patronizing comment. He knew that I thrived on new experiences, and often teased me about them. We laughed for a bit, and for that moment, I forgot about all the romantic drama we had been through in the past month. As we stood there alone in the street, I almost felt like I could kiss him and start this romance all over again, and I could feel the intensity between us as we stood there, gazing in each other's eyes.

But before we could make another move, there was some commotion just around the corner. Through the sound of taxis and club revelers, I could hear whispers in the alleyway. The clinking of our bike locks overshadowed the voices, but I could make out the distinct tone of several women.

"Tristan, shhh . . . Do you hear that?"

"Hear what?"

"Those voices. There are some women. Shhhh."

We peered around the corner of the street and noticed a group of about five or six women in burkas arguing in forced whispers amongst each other.

"Are you sure we should do this?" one of them whispered. "What if we get caught?"

"We're completely fucked if they find us," another one pleaded.

"I will beat you if you open your mouth. You shouldn't have come if you didn't want to go out with us. Now just drop your covering and let's go." The other women agreed, pushing the two timid girls to go along with the plan. They removed their burkas in the alleyway. What emerged were some of the most beautiful Middle Eastern women I had ever seen, in various shades of Hervé Leger bandage mini-dresses and five-inch Christian Louboutin heels. They dumped their holy cloths in a pile on the sidewalk and strutted to the front of the line. We stared in shock as the leader of the pack tapped the bouncer on the shoulder.

"Oui, mademoiselle?" he asked in a no-nonsense way. One of the vixens whispered something in the bouncer's ears. He smiled in a sordid way, amused at the group of Muslim girls dressed in the most unorthodox way. I watched in astonishment as he waved them into the club.

"Are they serious?" I gasped. Tristan nodded in familiarity.

"Stash and dash. Everybody needs to have a little fun, no?"

"But aren't they afraid that they'll get caught?"

"I doubt the men of the house are anywhere near France. They're probably in the Middle East or something.

"But I'm sure the men have spies to check on their women."

"I don't know how these women make the arrangement, but they do it." I was fascinated and wanted to know more about these stunning ladies. Once inside, Tristan and I took a seat at a dark corner of the bar to quietly observe the women. We watched as they sat at a table and ordered several bottles of Veuve Cliquot, Belvedere vodka, and Patron.

"Those girls sure know how to drink," I observed to Tristan.

"No, they aren't drinking. It's to attract a crowd. It's all for show. They aren't even here to drink."

"Well, at least their men are taking care of them financially. That liquor arsenal must cost a small fortune!" I watched as a few Frenchmen surrounded their table, trying to strike up a conversation. One of the men pulled the lead girl to a dark corner of the club and danced seductively as Fifty Cent's "Candy Shop" played in the background. I watched as the man coolly lifted up her dress to reveal her cleanly shaven pubic area, and she turned her head around to kiss him on the mouth. I nudged Tristan, who quietly sipped on a glass of Jameson on ice. He was watching too, but seemed disinterested.

"Do you see them?" I asked. I was shocked as the Muslim girl grabbed the man's friend, kissing him deeply while unbuckling his pants. "It's like they don't care if they get caught."

Tristan shrugged his shoulders. I watched in astonishment as she leaned down and fellated him, while the man behind her fucked her in the ass.

"This can't be happening. Is this really happening?" I asked, completely beside myself.

"This is what they do," Tristan told me, "so that they remain virgins, technically. They only do anal and blowjobs."

"Well, okay then. That's a revelation to me. I guess there's a whole lot going on under all those veils."

"Yeah, let's get out of here. I'm sick of seeing these fake women. I want to go someplace and listen to some real music." Tristan took my hand and led me out of the club. "Let's bike a little more. I know a nice Moroccan tea place not far from here where we can relax and talk a little. And they have live musicians." I agreed and mounted my bike for a tranquil night ride down the Rue St. Denis.

~

My stay in Paris had finally come to an end. I had just finished packing the last of my overflowing suitcases and was ready to settle in with a leftover croissant and some dark chocolate pudding I picked up at the local Monoprix. Tristan was in his room, organizing old CDs and rummaging through his music collection. He came out into the living room, covered in dust, with a charming grin on his face. I thought I had moved on as we had not been intimate for so many weeks, but looking at him in that moment brought back all of the intense sensual feeling I had about him for so long.

"I'm feeling a little hungry," he said. "Let's go get something to eat."

"Sure. Are we going by bike?"

"No, I think we can take the moped tonight." I was wearing one of my paper-thin air dresses, covered in an exotic array of deep orange and yellow. The neckline plunged just so that I revealed enough skin not to be scandalous. It was a perfect dress for the late August heat and would feel perfect as I rode, straddled on the back of Tristan's motorcycle. He tapped me on my thigh. "Let's go."

Tristan traced his ride over the roads of Paris, just like he did that night when I first arrived in Paris to meet him for the first time. He took his time winding in and out of roads, so that I could fully appreciate the lights of the Opera, the Gardens, and even the Tower, for what might have been our last time together. We rode up to Montmartre and through Pigalle, thoroughly enjoying the sleepy, near-empty Parisian streets, until we finally reached our destination, in a cozy corner of Île de la Cité with Notre Dame Cathedral as a romantic backdrop. Inside the restaurant, Tristan took the liberty of ordering us each a glass of red wine.

"I think this would go nicely with our dinner. But first, I want you to try something. Since I know you like new experiences."

"I'll let you guide the way. You're the expert." The waiter arrived, and Tristan gave him the order, and when the appetizer arrived, he laughed at my quizzical face.

"Escargot." He took the snail, scooping its soft body out of its shell with the tiny fork and offered it to me.

"Open your mouth." He placed the slimy creature on my tongue and I tasted the bits of garlic and butter as I chewed on the sinewy body before swallowing the tasteless morsel. I shook my head.

"I'm not a fan. But thanks for the experience." We ate our dinner in relative silence, stealing short glances over candlelight, and savoring the quiet intimate mood. Before long, we were finished, and we rode quietly home.

~

"Are you ready to go back to Brooklyn?" Tristan asked me, sitting beside me on the bed.

"I really don't want to go home, but I think it's time for me to start the next chapter of my life."

"I wasn't a good host, I know. I'm sorry for everything that happened." I nodded and crawled beside him to rest my head on his chest. "There are just so many things between us. So many things that I want to say, but I can't express them in the right words."

Tristan leaned in and kissed me on the shoulder. I returned his advance and we wrapped our bodies around each other, undressing until our naked skin touched. I stared at our bodies, his pale crème against my rich brown coffee tone, and then I gazed into his eyes. He kissed me, and cupped my breasts in his hand so that he could suck on my nipples. The sensation was sweet, and I reveled in the passionate emotion that filled my heart and body.

Tristan took his time with me, kissing every open space on my body from my neck to between my toes. He kissed the tender spaces between my thighs and lingered luxuriously on my tender clit, stroking his tongue gently over and around it so that I came profusely on his lips. I climbed on top of him, kissing his pink nipples, and stroking my tongue over his lithe body. He moaned as I bit his stomach and thighs before finally taking his entire cock in my mouth. I stroked him deeply until I could feel him harden in my mouth, and I could taste a drop of creamy saltiness from the pre-come that he released into my mouth. Before he could fully ejaculate, Tristan pulled me underneath his body and kissed me deeply. I kept my eyes open, poring over all his features, and he entered me forcefully, thrusting slowly and deeply while staring intently into my eyes.

It was good-bye sex.

NÃO FALO PORTUGUÊS

I had long admired the stealthy bodies of the Brazilian dancers who shimmied in their six-inch platforms. Often, before my other dance classes, I would sit on a bench outside the Samba class, and stare at them in envy, doing their dance with their tight abs and heart-shaped butts. When I was a young girl, I remembered reading an article in Allure Magazine about the mythic Brazilian butt. The image was the picture of a bulbous rear in a fuchsia thong, with an upside-down heart drawn on it. I had been in love with Brazil ever since. I later became entranced by the country's history and its rich African population. It was a pity that so many of the African dancers could never make the correlation between West African dance and traditional Brazilian dance. I felt like an insider knowing their true connection. I became more entranced with this culture as it was another welcome diversion from my African lover, of whom I had grown less and less fond with each sexual rendezvous. At this point in my life, my career was obviously not at the forefront of my ambitions, and I worked freelance design jobs to pay the bills and support my traveling habit.

No sooner had returned home from my dramatic experience in Paris had I booked a flight to Bahia, Brazil, on a whim and a dream. I arrived in Bahia via Sao Paulo, where the bulk of tourists were traveling. Thankfully, there was a driver waiting for me when I arrived at the small airport in the early, balmy evening. I whisked through the corridor of long arching palm trees in the small car that Jean-Paul, the owner of the bed and breakfast at which I would be staying, is driving. It is deliciously warm, and

I welcome the calm heat through my sweat suit that had only hours before shielded me from the brisk New York autumn air. As we drove along, the soft breeze soothed my mind and cooled my body, and I luxuriated in the fragrant air. Brazil. Even the pronunciation of the country filled me with thoughts of seduction and nights of hip grinding to the infectious samba drums.

The owner of the pousada directed me to my room, which was locked using an old skeleton key. I twisted the key and could smell the smoky dust coming from the hinges of the wooden door. My room was wonderfully simple. The bed was fitted with a blue nautical motif, and a white crochet comforter lay on top. The nightstand had a simple lamp, with cowry shells decorating its shade. I glanced around before I did anything. I dropped my bags and fell onto the plain, firm bed. My body melted into the lightly-scented sheets, and I could feel a breeze from the roofless bathroom. Adjacent to the bathroom was a hammock, resting just beneath the paneless window, so that I could just make out a few glimmering stars.

I peeled off my clothes, and took a shower in the open stall as the strong water pellets bounced off my body, and I began to feel my eyelids close. Somehow, I made it back to the hammock and drifted off to sleep.

~

The sun was shining so brightly the following day, I was

positive that I had slept through the entire morning. I scrambled to check the time and was relieved to see that it was only 8:30 a.m. I guess at this latitude the sun rose earlier and stayed out longer. It was easy to see why the locals never left. I took another, longer hot shower, and this time, I reveled in my nakedness as the soothing water ran over my body. I felt softer, pliable, free. I took the time to slather my body, first in shea butter, then coconut oil, and a dab of jojoba oil to finish. I buffed my skin and slipped on a blue cotton halter dress and sandals and went downstairs to check my e-mail and have breakfast. In the daylight I could get a better feel for the pousada. The wooden floors creaked softly beneath me with a vintage charm that was homey and rustic. I could smell the rich scent of roasting coffee and cinnamon coming from below. A young boy was talking in French to his mother, who happened to be the proprietor's wife. It was a nice setup, and I could have stayed there for weeks on end. When I made it downstairs to the parlor room, I noticed two black women speaking English. I was pleasantly surprised to find a couple of Black American sisters venturing out just like me, and staying at the same pousada. Though I was accustomed to traveling alone, I welcomed the idea of exploring the city—if only for a few hours—with a couple of like-minded women.

The friends made a cute pair, one with smooth chocolate skin and a closely shaven head of soft blond curls, the other with chestnut-colored locs that framed her caramel latte complexion.

"I'm Sandra and this is my girl Sasha," the woman with the locs chimed. "We're from D.C. It's my birthday and we're here to celebrate. Have you seen the men down here? Girl, let me tell you . . ." she started as we proceeded to the breakfast table where another gentleman sat eating breakfast. The man was visibly older, and white, and gave off a kind of hippy vibe. He glanced up at us, averting his attention from the blazing morning sun that shone through the windows onto the breakfast table. It was a wonderful spread, and we gasped at the array of delicious foods before us: mangoes, papayas, bananas, juices, yogurt, granola, eggs. My stomach growled in anticipation of the tropical feast. The woman continued while we all sat eating and listening to the story.

"So we met these two fine guys in Pelourinho. I mean they were delicious. One was light, and the other was chocolate. They both were completely ripped. Girl . . ." Sandra sucked her teeth and Sasha laughed in agreement. "So these guys, they took us out for lunch in the city center, and we had a blast. And then, they were like, 'There's a block party happening down in our hood. You should come.' We were down, because we like to explore and have a good time, so we agreed to go. They gave us the address, and we took a taxi down there. We kept driving, and driving, and we were like, where the hell are we going? Girl, do you know we ended up in the fucking barrio! And then, the party didn't start until like, midnight! So we stayed until more people came, and then slipped out. That was crazy."

"They could have done anything to us. What the hell were we thinking?" Sasha added. The women laughed in unison. "Live and learn. So what are your plans?" Sasha asked me.

"Well, I'm a dancer, and I really wanted to try and get in a dance class while I'm here. I also wanted to check out a show by the Ballet Folklorico. That show is tonight. I wanted to spend a day on the island of Itaparica, too. Have you been?"

"Yes, we loved it," Sasha responded emphatically. "It is absolutely beautiful, and the boat ride is the best. You'll love it."

"Tell you what," Sandra added, "Let's meet up here at around ten and then we can go out for a drink and some dancing."

"Sounds good," I replied. The ladies quickly finished their breakfast and quietly left the house for their adventures, leaving me alone with the other traveler. I introduced myself between bits of succulent mango and honeydew melon.

"So, what's your name?" The man slowly averted his gaze from the tantalizing skyline and responded.

"Hi there, I'm Gary. I'm sorry, I was just in a trance over this scenery."

"I know, isn't it amazing? I think I could stay here forever!"

"How long are you staying?"

"Only for five days. I'm here for my birthday.

"Five days? That's entirely too short. You have to stay here for a month for it to really sink in. Your whole body and train of thought begins to change."

"I can believe it. Unfortunately, work and money don't permit me to stay longer, but I do plan to visit again one day when neither is a factor."

"It will be well worth it. For me, this is my life. I'm originally from Seattle, but I'm living in Spain right now. I used to be a food connoisseur and I ran several restaurants in the States before I got into the hotel business. I run a set of luxury resorts in Ibiza. Have you heard of Ibiza?" He pronounced the city Ih-BEE-tha. I took it as being the correct version of what I had mispronounced for so many years.

"Ah Ibiza, yes, I heard that was a hardcore party city." "Oh yes, lots of drugs and parties. The drugs and parties rival Goa in India. But the vibe is definitely European, rich, and a little trashy. Of course, my resorts are none of the sort." He handed me one of his business cards. It was a heavy cardstock, and the name of the company, Luxur Resorts, was embossed in gold leaf. "When you decide to visit Spain, give me a call and I'll set you up in one of my villas. You won't be disappointed." I noted the company in my journal with the intent of visiting Spain and staying in a luxurious villa overlooking the Mediterranean. It was yet another travel fantasy for me to fulfill.

"Thanks, I will keep you in mind. So what are you plans while you're here?"

"Well, I found this musician in Pelourinho playing some badass drums on the street. His family owns a music shop and he was going to give me a few drum lessons. He should be arriving here soon, and we'll take a cab over to their shop. He and his father are masters—or so they told me—so I think I'm getting a deal on private lessons."

~

That day, my goal was to visit the island of Itaparica, off the coast of Salvador, Bahia. I took a bus downtown and took a lift down to where I could catch a boat that left hourly to the island. As I sat waiting on the dock, I caught notice of a trio of delicious-looking Brazilian men: two were sun-kissed mulattoes, and the one in the middle was a deep chocolate.

He was bald, and had softly swollen, pink lips. I wondered what it would be like to kiss them. He was laughing with his buddies, and when he smiled, an imperfectly radiant set of pearly white teeth shone in his mouth. He caught me staring at him, and I quickly averted my gaze. The captain hollered an order and the Brazilian locals rushed to the boat to find an empty seat for the short journey to the island.

The water over the Atlantic was stunning. The brisk sea air tousled my hair, and I squinted as the powerful rays from the sun reflected off the crystal blue waters. I looked down, and could almost see clear to the bottom of the ocean. It was magic. I gazed out into the endless horizon and drifted into a daydream.

The sound of shattered glass broke my trance. A few men had gotten overly intoxicated and started breaking bottles for the hell of it. Two guards moved them to the lower deck of the boat, and in the midst of all the commotion, the chocolate brother slid next to me.

"Hi, how are you?"

"I'm fine, thank you." I didn't want to sound too eager.

"My name is Binho, what's yours?" He spoke in the sexiest

broken English, and smiled, embarrassed at his mispronunciation. He tried in vain to pronounce my name and settled on a nickname for me. "I call you . . . Garota Chocolate." Just by hearing the word chocolate, I knew it had something to do with my skin, which was glistening in the sun due to the melting shea and olive oils on my body. I smiled at him again, taking in the breadth of his beauty. "Where are you from?" he asked.

"Los Estados Unidos," I replied. I cursed myself for not having bothered to learn a little more Portuguese before coming. I smiled at him again. "So, where are you going now?"

"I visit my family on Itaparica." He pointed to the two males and a female, sitting across from us on the boat. "They are my cousins, and she is my sister. I looked their way and nodded. If you want, you come visit my family? We have a party for my grandmother on the beach." I agreed, haphazardly. I figured I've been in worse situations, and if I were going to die, at least it would be in paradise. We sat on the boat, quietly admiring the panoramic views until it was time to disembark.

From the boat we walked past the tourist area with the overpriced restaurants and shops for about a quarter mile until we got to a portion with several streets and houses owned by the locals. Children played soccer in the streets, and in the near distance, I could hear the tap of the samba drums. The salty breeze carried its way through the town, and the sun's warmth was accommodating. We finally made it to the house, and immediately I was greeted by an older woman, and several other relatives. I was relieved to see that Binho was telling the truth. The house was a ruckus of running, playing children, barking dogs, samba music, and rowdy drunk men. One of Binho's uncles was handling the grill while holding fast to an ice-cold bottle of Skol. He offered me a perfectly cooked sausage.

I took in the atmosphere as one of Binho's cousins offered me a beer. Almost no one spoke any English, so I was surprised that these people had allowed me to come to their house and party. Binho's aunt prepared a plate of rice and beans and potato salad to go along with my sausage. If I didn't know it, I could have been at any random block party in Spanish Harlem. After a while, Binho approached me and lightly grabbed my arm.

"Do you want to go to the beach? I want to swim." I thought of the thong swimsuit I was wearing underneath my sundress. I had gotten it as part of the gift bag at a recent Rosa Cha fashion show. The blue tie-dye bikini matched my dress perfectly, and the fit hugged and exposed each and every curve, covering my ass just enough so that it was an almost-thong, but not a full-on string. In the United States, it would be riotous to wear such a suit. But looking at the women on the streets of Bahia, I could tell that the attitude was anything goes. More importantly, I wanted to see Binho's reaction to me in the swimsuit. I could already tell where our little excursion was going, and I agreed to fully partake in any libertine activity in Brazil. We walked a short distance from the house to the beach, where I lifted my dress over my head and placed it in my sun bag. The men who had been idling with their families stopped to stare. They gave Binho the thumbs up as he stared at my nearly naked body.

"Wow," he sighed. "Bonita." I walked along the beach, gaining pride with every step. When we neared the edge of the beach he took off his white tank top and cargo shorts to reveal a skimpy black speedo. There was a muscle on every inch of his dark-chocolate body, and I stared in admiration. I felt a little exposed, as I had never been so bold as to wear such a skimpy suit in public. No one seemed to notice. We walked down the beach, and I noticed some of the men smiling at me, admiringly. I loved the way they stared, and the way they commented was in the most flattering, unassuming way. I wasn't to used to all of this pure adoration. The men in Brooklyn were animals; they could never gracefully compliment a woman. In Bahia, I actually felt truly, and naturally, sexy.

"Come into the water with me." He held out his hand. We waded out to an empty space in the ocean and I noticed a few families here and there, playing happily in the water.

"I don't know how to swim," I confessed.

"I will show you." He grabbed both of my palms. "Press down on my hands and lift your feet off the ground." I lifted one leg up, and then the other, cautiously. As I wobbled in the water, my butt bobbled just above the ocean's surface, like two sea marbles. I rocked unsteadily as he laughed, "Relax."

I lifted my feet off the ocean floor so that I floated in the ocean, and in my clumsiness, I stumbled into his face. We kissed playfully, and I scanned the family nearby, who were cautiously watching us as we played in the water. I saw the father give us a look of disapproval as Binho and I kissed more passionately. I lowered my feet back down from sea level and wrapped my legs around his waist. He pressed his hips against mine, and slid his hands down my back and into my bikini bottom, while I reached for the condom I had placed in a hidden compartment in my bikini. Unwrapping it underwater, I looked around for any onlookers, and seeing that the family had swam away, I slipped the tip of the condom in my mouth and dove underwater, skillfully unraveling the latex onto his hardened cock. I emerged to kiss him passionately on his plump lips and he seamlessly slipped his cock inside me with steady, rhythmic thrusts. I wrapped my arms around his shoulders for leverage, and we laughed as we engaged in our pleasure. I looked away from Binho to see the father of the family give us a look of disapproval once more, and we just laughed.

Still connected, Binho walked with me deeper into the sea, and we continued fucking, his thrusts deepening the farther we slipped into the ocean. I came before him, but when he experienced his orgasm, he shuddered, I was sure his body would give out onto the ocean floor. I quickly dismounted him, pecked him on the lips, and walked back toward the shore to lie in the sun and savor my orgasm. Binho took a swim for a few more moments, and came back onto the shore to lie beside me. We spoke very little, but we needed no words to express our pleasure. A young boy was selling beers on the beach, and Binho signaled for him to come by. He bought two Skols for us and we enjoyed the chilly refreshment. As the sun began to dip, I realized that I needed to go back to the mainland. Binho gave me his number, so that we could meet up later that evening in Pelourinho. I knew there was a slim chance of that actually happening, but I took his number anyway and promised to call.

~

I made it back to the pousada in just enough time to bathe and get ready for my evening in town. I wasn't sure what the ladies had planned, but I knew I had to see some dancing. The Ballet Folklorico de Bahia was an internationally renowned dance company that explored traditional Brazilian dance. Before I left the States for Bahia, I had been taking some traditional Samba classes, and I was beginning to really dig the African rhythms in the new, sexy, alternate style. It was a welcome reprieve from the thunderous, quick-paced movements of the West African dances to which I was accustomed. I quickly dressed and walked into Pelourinho for the show. For some reason, I had felt emboldened and unafraid of walking by myself at night in this city. I felt like it was my city, my home, and the welcoming remarks I got as I strolled the cobbled streets in my sturdy Havainas flip flops further reinforced my mood.

I thought of Binho and the wonderful sex we had that afternoon. I felt warm, sexy, and free with this whole experience and even made a half-hearted attempt to contact him that evening, although the call never went through. I thought about the man I loved at home in New York, and whom He was fucking when I wasn't around. No matter where I seemed to be in the world, He was always on my mind, pervading my thoughts, curtailing my actions, and being an ever-present figure in my life. I just couldn't let Him go, no matter where I traveled. Here in the sexy streets of Bahia, this man seemed to saturate my thoughts more than ever.

~

I found my way to the Ballet theater and made my way in. No one seemed to have purchased tickets ahead of time, so the ticket sales were on a first come, first serve basis. Most of the theater-goers were white tourists, in search of the exotic cultural experience. I was one of the few people of color there to witness the show. While the rest of the crowd sat tepidly in their bleacher seats inside the small theater, I crept towards the front and sat on the stage floor, to get a full sense of the movement, and to feel the pulse of their footsteps beneath my pelvic bone. I wanted to be immersed in their rhythm.

The theater darkened and I watched those muscular, glowing black and brown bodies make love on the stage, their shapes intertwined in rhythmic, pulsating movements. *Make love.* I missed making love. Suddenly, a dancer bolted from behind the audience, his body completely except for a pair of fitted spandex shorts. The

European tourists who were watching the show from the side of the stage seemed startled and amused by what they surely thought were "primitives." I stared on, aroused by his command of the stage, and his toned, lithe, black body. The ballet ended to thunderous applause, and each company member invited an audience member onto the stage to dance. I quickly slid out of the small theater among the commotion, and made my way into the streets teeming with tourists and local people selling their wares in the historic center. I walked to the center of Pelourinho looking for a bar and some good food, wandering around the cobbled streets, staring at the brightly colored buildings in their Spanish-inspired architectural style. In one of the corners of the city square, I spotted a pair of women arguing with a taxi driver. He apparently had driven them around in circles and was demanding an inflated fare for his services. I looked harder and made out the faces of Sandra and Sasha, the two other black women that were staying at the pousada. I ran up to them.

"Hey guys, what's going on?"

"Oh my God. We just wanted to get a ride from the pousada to the center! And he drove us all over the place!" I laughed.

"Why did you hail a cab? You do realize you could *walk* from the pousada to the center, right? I just did and it's a ten-minute walk!" They laughed at the silliness of the situation and paid the cab driver. "It seems like you ladies keep getting into tangled situations. Do you travel often?"

"Yeah, we've traveled. I think we're just having a run of

bad luck," Sandra responded. "How was your day?" I proceeded to tell them all about the beautiful island of Itaparica without divulging my little sexual escapade with Binho. I secretly hoped that I would bump into him on this hot Saturday night. I felt especially sexy and wanted an escort for the rounds of dancing and drinking that we would inevitably have in town.

"Sounds amazing. We were looking for a place to dance. We already ate back at the pousada. What about you?"

"Well the guy, Binho, introduced me to his entire family. They were having a birthday celebration for one of the younger children, and they barbecued out on the beach. It was delicious. I mean, they kept stuffing me with pork sausages, rice, and potato salad. It was just like being at home!"

"You see, we need to have those kinds of experiences. Instead, we get invited to the ghetto where nobody has any money and we end up paying for our own food," Sasha laughed.

"Sorry about that guys. I just got really lucky. And there was so much beer, it was amazing I didn't pass out drunk with these strangers. I think the only thing I spent money on today was the cost of the boat ticket to the island!" I couldn't help but go on about my amazing experience with these women that I had just met. "I don't know about you ladies, but I am definitely in the mood for some dancing."

"Dancing sounds perfect," Sandra agreed. We walked around the crowded center and found a small club filled with locals and cheap beer. We sat at a small, nondescript table near the back of the open-air club and waited for the bartender to serve us a standard bottle of Skol. We caught the attention of a few delicious-looking Brazilian men standing in the corner, drinking and playing a game of pool near the open-air bar. I took the chance to jump in the middle of the dance floor and grind my hips with some of the basic samba moves I had learned at the Alvin Ailey Center back in New York. I wasn't a pro, but my hips did the work for me, and before I knew it, I was surrounded by other revelers and a fair-skinned Brazilian man who embraced me and grinded his body against mine as we did our soft samba groove.

~

My final day in Bahia arrived and I could have cried as I packed my suitcase to go. I had picked up a few instruments to take home with me: a few small shakers, a Brazilian rain stick etched with proverbs in Portuguese, a small samba drum, and a berimbau, a stringed instrument with a gourd at the tip that all the hot capoeira fighters strummed along the coastline.

Before my cab arrived for my ride to the airport, I took one final bus ride down to the seashore and stripped down to my skimpiest bikini. A merchant selling snacks and body oil on the beach offered to take a picture of me as I splashed around in the ultra-blue waters. My face was wet from the salt water, but I cried my own tears of joy as I looked out onto the Atlantic. I kneeled in

the water and kissed my hands to the sun.
        "Obrigada, Brazil."

CLINIC

When I got back from Brazil, I immediately scheduled an appointment for my biannual HIV test. I had made it a protocol for me to visit the STD clinic, and after the first few times, I had no shame. It was as standard for me as a dental appointment. You went in, got your blood drawn, and an hour later you got a paper stating a clean bill of health, if you were lucky. I often walked around with this sheet of paper in my wallet to display if the situation arose. If I was going to be having sex, then I needed to get tested. Tests were a part of my transient lifestyle.

But something about this visit made me want to rethink this break-neck speed and whether or not it was all worth it. I had protected sex with all of my international lovers, but the one who scared me the most was Abdoulaye, the one who lived right in my own backyard. We had been fucking on and off all this time and I had been lucky that all my tests always came back negative considering his endless conveyor belt of lovers. But how long would it be before the results revealed something positive? I didn't want to risk my health anymore, but I couldn't find the strength to fully break away from this man who held complete control over my life without even placing a finger on my body. I could be a thousand miles away and he would still manage to find me, calling me as soon as my plane touched the tarmac, or if I happened to visit another dance class in the city. Even at events that were unrelated to dance, I managed to bump into one of his other lovers, or an associate. He had permeated every corner of my life and I had foolishly allowed it. He had fucked my body and my mind.

I wondered how many of his other women got tested, or if they even bothered at all. They all seemed so smitten with him. After all, he seemed like the perfect embodiment of health, with his chiseled arms and his potent virility. I remember proudly meeting up with him one time to show him my negative test results. He shrugged with indifference and said he trusted his intuition. How could he be sick? I wanted to believe that he was a healthy man, but the smart side of me made sure I maintained my clinic visits. I may have been a fool for love, but I would not destroy my health because of this man.

I walked into the office in a blank building on Flatbush Avenue, grabbed a pink intake card with a number, and sat down. Looking around the room, I saw a variety of young people. There were a pair of late-twenty-something white women, a group of black teenage girls who sat solemnly, and a handful of black men. It was early. I was always one of the first ones in the clinic. If I got in when it opened at eight-thirty, I could be out by ten. The later in the day you came, the longer you waited. Not long after, the imbeciles would arrive, laughing and joking about the prior evening's conquests. I sat staring at the grainy HIV prevention video, waiting for the intake counselor to call my number. Not long after my arrival, a group of rowdy young men strolled into the clinic. Two were husky Dominicans and the other two were equally brawny black men. The slanted caps and oversized jackets partially hid their identity, while their boisterous voices permeated the room. They had obviously spent the weekend clubbing, and I could smell the faint hint of ganja in the air that followed them to their seats. An orderly came out and yelled the first two numbers. The white girls stood up and went in for the obligatory chat and check-in with a peer counselor. After a few minutes they came back out and sat in another set of chairs. Already the clinic was becoming crowded, and seats were at a premium. I filled out the pink card, and no sooner had I completed my last pen stroke did the orderly announce my number.

I went into the cluttered government employee office. There was a young woman there, probably in her late twenties. She sat, staring blankly at a data-entry computer screen while the tinker of a radio playing *Steve Harvey's Morning Show* hummed in the background. There were HIV prevention flyers and various phone numbers posted on her wall. I handed her my card, and she began entering my information.

"Have you been here before?"

"Yes, six months ago," I replied.

"Oh, so you're coming in for a follow-up, basically." I nodded, thinking about all the crazy shit I had done in the past six months. If I tested positive for anything, it probably wouldn't show up for another six months.

"Do you have any pain? Any burning? Itching? Funny discharge?" I shook my head. "No, but I'd like to be tested for everything anyway."

"Okay, go back to the sitting room, and listen for your number. You'll have to do a urine test as well. The doctor will be in the office shortly."

I sat, waiting impatiently for my number to be called, thinking of all the millions of things I needed to do. I didn't even call into my new freelance job to tell them I would be late that morning. I figured I would just slip into my corner of the office when no one was looking. I had no major work to do anyway, and I was basically a good employee. No one ever suspected the good employee of mischief. I thought of the times in my teenage years when I dated a series of older teenage boys. All times of the day, especially in the summertime, these boys would call the house phone. We would come up with codes for the call, so that I would eventually know who was contacting me at any given time. Sometimes my parents would pick up the receiver, look quizzically into the air, and then hang up. I loved boys. They were my secret vice, and I would hide my sinful pleasures with them by excelling in school, making the honor roll, and sitting on the student council. It's always the quiet ones, they say.

About twenty minutes later, the phlebotomist came out and flatly called my number. I walked into her room and sat on an empty clinical chair, one arm severely worn from where countless arms had rested and been poked for blood specimens. I don't know if the lady hated her job, or hated me, but she was always pissed off, as if all the men and women who came in to get tested were nameless, faceless city scum with no value, and no importance. I imagined that this mulatto woman, maybe in her late forties, with thick black natural ringlets pulled back into a bun, probably had a daughter who went to St. Ann's High School, vacationed in Europe on holidays, and had a condo in Windsor Terrace. She would never find her daughter in these clinics because the likes of these people, who came to her office everyday, were beneath her. The phlebotomist raised a bitchy brow.

"Are you just in here for HIV?" I shook my head. "I'm actually getting the full works today. For good measure." She sighed and looked at my intake slip.

"Sit back, put your hand out, and make a fist." I interrupted her. "Excuse me, but what happened to the swabs?" I was used to having her instruct me to swab the inside of my cheek with a tab, and place it inside a tube.

"We're not doing those right now. It turns out that some of those tests were reading false-positive. Now. Place your right hand over your left arm and hold it in place. I don't need you jerking up and squirting blood all over my office."

I had pissed her off without doing anything. She took a needle and handily drew blood from my arm. She then took a gauze strip and instructed me to apply pressure to it while she placed a Band-Aid over the puncture. Turning away from me, she placed a label on my specimen and shooed me out of her office. "Your results will be ready in about an hour depending on how busy we get. You can go back to the waiting room," she said listlessly.

By now the small clinic was full of rambunctious teenagers and party-going men. It sounded like the intersection of Nostrand and Fulton Avenues. All kinds of people filled the seats, reading the free city papers, talking on their cells, and annoyingly using their two-ways, so that everyone could hear the contents of their mundane conversations. I didn't want to be in the vicinity of these fools anymore. Even then, I began to see myself as better than they. I had goals and ambitions, and they didn't only include what I would be wearing to the club that weekend. The wild sex with random partners had to stop, or pretty soon my results wouldn't be so clean, but it wasn't a new life of monogamy that I wanted. I longed for a loving, caring relationship, in which sex wasn't the only common denominator. I wanted to love and be loved, fully, freely, and seriously. I didn't want to be the sideline ho, the weekend freak, the go-to party gal. I was worth more than that.

I quickly diverted the reflections of my relationship goals towards my agenda for the day. Work, then a quick trip to the farmer's market, a quick pedicure, then dance class. Everything I did in New York revolved around getting to dance class in time. I'm not sure if I was excited to see Abdoulaye or to do what I loved, which was dancing. My days never ended earlier than two a.m., when, after dance class, we would often meet at a diner on the Upper West Side, and then have sex at his apartment. I always wondered in the back of my mind what his wife thought of all his late-night trysts. Surely she didn't believe that he was out rehearsing or performing at some random gig every night. The only time he didn't go out with me—or with one of his many lovers—was on a Sunday. Sunday, he proclaimed, was the day he spent with family.

As I thought about this I began to drift back into the raw emotion of what my love life had become. I never allowed myself to use that term, love. I didn't love Abdoulaye, I was infatuated with him, I assured myself. But I knew deep down that I had truly been the fool and fallen in love. Women weren't equipped to be players. How was it that I had allowed myself to be a part of a destructive relationship, in which I was debased on nearly a daily basis with a series of loveless sexual transactions? I had become one of the class bitches whom I hated, the ones who preened and fought for a spot in front of the studio mirrors, all while fucking the same man. I had thought that by standing alone in a corner, and being inconspicuous, that I would be less suspect. I would openly criticize him, and even stopped attending his classes. But everybody knew that I was one of his concubines. I wore the horrible scarlet letter, and I tried desperately for months to erase it. Maybe, I thought, this was the reasoning behind my travels. Maybe it was the idea of escaping the life I had created in New York City, for something foreign, exotic, and unchallenging. Maybe I was avoiding the cancer in my life that I could easily be cured of, if I would only just quit him.

A short woman in her fifties, bottle blond, and heavily made up, called my number for the urine test. She took me out into the hallway and gave me instructions on how to pee in the cup and where to drop my specimen. In the bathroom, there was a young black girl, a teenager, who was holding her cup of urine solemnly and staring in the mirror in front of the sink. She looked at me and shifted so that I could get in the stall in the small bathroom. As I peed, I saw the bottom of her shoes as she stood there, motionless. I continued listening as she opened the door and walked out, into the hallway. How was it that I, supposedly so much older, so much wiser, was in the same place as she was? Wild and confused, proud and remorseful. Like a fawn in the desert. After all my travels, navigating complex cities and unpopulated jungles, dusty, winding mountains and palace labyrinths, I was lost.

I walked back into the triage room with my specimen, handed it to the orderly, and sat back down, in another seat. The loud Dominican came out of the administrator's office.

"I'm all clear!" he exclaimed to the other anonymous clients in the waiting room. His crew was waiting for him in the back. "I'm having wild sex tonight, my nigga! Raw!" I cringed at the foolishness, looking on while he laughed boisterously, gathering congratulatory handshakes from his homeboys. I heard my number being called by the orderly. The doctor had arrived.

PARIS ENDINGS

I contemplated my next romantic move, even though common sense told me that I should be alone to assess the things that I truly desired. Though my time in Paris ended on a good note with Tristan, I knew deep down inside that he was emotionally troubled, and wrestled with the dilemma of loving two women. Tristan wasn't a sure bet, but I could at least try to see where his heart lie by making a final visit.

I returned to Paris the following winter to complete this unfinished business but I ultimately knew that I needed to let Tristan go. He was planning a hiking trip in the mountains, and wanted to order a specialty Patagonia parka that couldn't be shipped to his address in Paris. I agreed to accept his shipment in Brooklyn, knowing that it would be my sole reason for visiting him in Paris on Valentine's weekend.

Tristan had given up his convenient apartment in Bastille, and instead decided to work on renovating a small studio that he had managed to purchase in Belleville. He was basically living in a sleeping bag among rodents, plywood, and cement blocks, so staying at his place was out of the question. Instead, he offered his younger brother's place, who happened to be out of town for that weekend. His apartment was a small studio in the fashionable Saint Germain des Prés section, neatly tucked away behind a grand set of wooden, arched doors with elaborately carved ornaments and a set of brass handles. I walked along the streets with my faithful Louis Vuitton duffel bag, passing a Sonia Rykiel shop, filled with color-blocked dresses. Fashion still made my heart leap at times, but this time I just stared at the window display in muted excitement. Fashion is what first brought me to Paris, but love is what always made me return. The premise of this trip was lame, but I needed any excuse to see Tristan, if only for one last time.

We decided to meet at a Vietnamese restaurant not far from his new apartment where we would exchange greetings over Bánh mìs.

I waited for him on a nondescript corner as I watched the evening crowd purchase their baguettes and rotisserie chickens for the evening's dinner. And then I saw him emerge from the crowd, his unmistakable brunette crew cut peeking out of his skullcap, his handsome, yet delicate features peering out from beneath his down jacket.

"Tristan!" I waved. He saw me, and instantly flashed a smile. We hugged briefly and gave each other a peck on each cheek.

"How are you? How is life?" Tristan asked.

"Everything is great! I started a new job. Making a bit more money, so not as poor as I was when I last saw you," I said.

"Yes, it's amazing you were able to stay as long as you did. You lived the fantasy artist life." We both laughed at this, and then stood in silence.

There was so much that I wanted to say, so many things that I had hoped for in this final meeting. But the words never came, and instead I handed him the parka.

"It shipped pretty fast!"

"Yes, I knew it would. Thank you so much. I appreciate this."

"Anytime." Again, silence. "So, when are you going on your trip?"

"Well, Emiline and I, we plan to go very soon, maybe next month."

The sound of her name made my heart sink. I knew it was bound to happen, their reconnection. I knew that I was only a fling, a happenstance, and that the connection between us was mostly sexual. But it still hurt nonetheless. I was Tristan's American experience.

"Okay, well have fun," I responded, as my voice cracked in the wind. I gave him a quick hug, and then quickly turned away to go in the opposite direction down the bustling Avenue Simon Bolivar, where no one would notice the lone tear streaming down my cold, hardened face.

~

A few days later, back in Brooklyn, I was sitting at home alone in my apartment, and I saw a message from Tristan. My heart skipped in anticipation of what his message might be. Was it a note of reconciliation, or a simple thank you? I hesitated a bit, then opened the e-mail.

TO: sxybrftdancer@yahoo.com
FROM: Tristan26@gmail.com
SUBJECT: Your friend from the Old Country

"Hi there. I want to thank you again for visiting me and bringing my coat to me. It will be very useful as we climb the mountains in Nepal. You should really try to scale a mountain sometime. Anyway, I was thinking of visiting Brooklyn in the fall. Can Emiline and I come and stay at your place while we are in New York?

The request was absurd. Did he not have any qualms about staying in the apartment of a woman whom he had fucked while he was on the outs with his main squeeze? Where was his discretion? I forwarded my best friend Shing-I the e-mail, to see if she thought the request was as crazy I thought.

TO: sxybrftdancer@yahoo.com
FROM: tofubutter@hotmail.com
SUBJECT: Re: FW: Your friend from the Old Country

This guy's an asshole. Ignore him.

Of course, I couldn't ignore the guy, but I had to let him know why it was unacceptable. I blind copied Shing-I so that she could get in on the action. I wanted to see what she really thought about the whole situation. Maybe he was truly clueless.

TO: Tristan26@gmail.com
FROM: sxbrftdncer@yahoo.com
BCC: tofubutter@hotmail.com

SUBJECT: Re: Your friend from the Old Country

Wow, I'm glad that you want to visit New York. There is so much to see in the fall. But I don't think it would be appropriate to bring Emiline along. It would be very uncomfortable for all of us, don't you think?

FROM: Tristan26@gmail.com
TO: sxybareftdncr@yahoo.com
SUBJECT: The Elementary Rules of Hospitality

Yes, I'm still coming. The question of being comfortable with Emiline only depends on what you did while you stayed in my home! You reap what you sow! Your response just shows me how disrespectful you are. You don't care about me and you obviously don't care about Emiline, of course. This situation highlights your philosophy of life: take of people (their money, their time, their boyfriend) give nothing, and make friends all over the world by persuading them that you care about them.

It's okay, I won't go to your place, alone or with Emiline. I'd rather spend time with people who are truly generous, rather than those people who live selfishly under a generous guise.

I never want to see or hear from you again.

Tristan

I was flabbergasted by his response. Not only did he throw me under the bus by blaming me for tearing apart his relationship, without taking any responsibility himself, but he also had the nerve to say that I used him, and that I was ungrateful for being allowed to stay with him in Paris. I could not believe this son of a bitch. I forwarded the e-mail to Shing-I to gauge her reaction.

TO: sxybrftdancer@yahoo.com
FROM: tofubutter@hotmail.com
SUBJECT: Re: FW: The Elementary Rules of Hospitality

Is he serious?? Please leave this guy alone. Your first response made perfect sense. What doesn't he understand?

FROM: sxybareftdncr@yahoo.com
TO: Tristan26@gmail.com
SUBJECT: Re: The Elementary Rules of Hospitality

Wow, I am sorry to have upset you. And I am really hurt that you feel this way. There is nothing that I could say or do to express my gratitude for everything you have done for me. You have gone above and beyond being a friend. And no, I don't make friends to use them or exploit what they have; you completely misinterpreted my intentions. If that's the type of person you really think I am, then you don't know me at all.

But don't you think it would be peculiar to come with your girlfriend to my home when there wasobviously tension when I did the same? Did you discuss this with Emiline? How does she feel

about it? Does she know that we slept together? It is understandable to me that Emiline would be upset about me staying with you when you didn't even tell her beforehand. Even if it is your place, the situation is uncomfortable, don't you understand that? Consider that while I was staying with you, I was just as uncomfortable. Which is why I had contemplated leaving at some point earlier, and why I stayed out of the house most of the time. What I had hoped would flourish as a romantic relationship was quickly squashed. So I was going through a lot, too. And I obviously put a strain on your relationship with Emiline. Do you honestly believe that the strain would not reemerge if she were here, in my home? Think about it.

Again, I am really hurt that you feel this way. I never tried to use you. Yes, it would be great for you to come, and save money, too. And I would open my door to you, but not to a repetition of what happened before. I thank you a thousand times over for all that you have done for me. I'd hate to lose our friendship, but if that's how you feel, then so be it.

xoxo

I hit send, and then sat back in my chair. I knew I would never get a response, and I was probably better off if I didn't. I

was through being the punching bag of assholes who lived double lives. I wanted to send a fuck you to all the assholes who ever
screwed me over. But mostly I wanted to send a giant Fuck You to
myself for allowing these men to disrespect me in the worst way.
But for now, I had this Frenchman on whom I could lay my anger.

"Fuck you, Tristan. And fuck Paris, too."

My love life was in shambles and my relationship with Abdoulaye was a drama-filled mess. So I once again used travel as a coping mechanism to ail my woes. I wanted to go someplace that was so far away and remote that no one would bother to reach me, especially Abdoulaye, whom I now hated. An Indian coworker suggested that I give her native land a try, and I was entranced by her descriptive visions of floating on a houseboat in Kerala, or exploring the jungles and beaches of Goa. May was the perfect time of year to go, in my opinion. It was just before the rainy season would hit, but just after the height of the tourist season in order to avoid the heightened fees on airfare and attractions.

The logistics of the trip were hazy, but with my travel experience, I knew I could figure it out. A few Indian friends suggested various destinations within the country, each one more fascinating than the next, so that after a few weeks I had developed a rough itinerary that spanned the entire western half of the country. I would start in New Delhi, make my way to Agra for a visit to the Taj Mahal, then Jaipur to visit the Old Pink City. Following that, I would jet to Goa for some deep greenery and seaside respite, followed by a boat ride in Kerala. Lastly, I would end in Bombay, where I would end my trip spectacularly in an over-the-top Indian resort, complete with elephant rides, snake charmers, and sword-eaters in my silly, fetishized fantasy. This trip was going to be unforgettable. I questioned whether I could do this trip by myself. I theorized that I had gone to Senegal without knowing whom I was staying with, and had stayed with a couple of Nigerian men and women that I barely knew, all for the thrill of the experience. What would be so hard about India?

I was waiting for the L train on the way to Williamsburg, Brooklyn one night, and I literally bumped into my ex-boyfriend, Elijah. It had been nearly two years since I last saw him in a dance class, and our breakup was particularly bad and a little juvenile. I wasn't exactly excited to see him standing on the platform. When I saw him, I quickly averted my eyes as I saw him approach me from my peripheral view. The train arrived at the platform, and when the doors opened, I jumped in and went directly to the center, where it was hardest to be reached, with the crush of riders jamming the train car. I put my headphones on and tried to act oblivious, but knew that he had seen me and would make his way to where I was standing. When he was standing directly beside me, I realized I couldn't ignore him, and mustered a hello. He smiled, and as the train jerked forward he fell into me and kissed me on the lips. The other passengers looked at us, the men in awe at Eli's flawless game. I was shocked and annoyed, but didn't want to make a scene.

His move was bold, charming, and a little irritating. Who the hell did he think he was rolling up on me and invading my space like that? I was so caught off-guard that I laughed nervously and looked around. The other women on the train looked at me with envy. Honestly, the brother was fine. His skin was a milk-kissed caramel, and his smile was near perfection. He wore his hair in dreadlocks that flowed down his back with a glossy sheen.

His skin glowed in the florescent train lighting, and he wore a tank top to show off his hard-earned biceps. He was a show pony, and at the right angle he looked like Shemar Moore with locs.

I remember the first time I met Eli. It was a warm summer night in late June and I was walking down 125th Street in Harlem. I stopped on the corner of Lenox, where a street vendor was selling bootleg DVDs and noticed Eli's orange neon MTA transit vest from the corner of my eye. It was the same vest that my stepfather had worn home several late nights after working the subway tunnels making repairs. I was attracted to Eli, but kept my eyes focused on the movie cases lying on a sheet on the ground. Well, at least he has a job, I thought.

"Nice dress," he said as he passed by. I smiled and nodded thank you, and returned my gaze to the DVD selections. I didn't want to seem too desperate. He got halfway down the block and then turned around. I could see him coming, and I got tense. The fact that this hot guy was about to approach me made me excited and a little apprehensive. I didn't think I was dressed very attractively to warrant the admiration of such a stud. He saddled beside me and pretended to browse the selection of porn videos that the dealer had artfully displayed on a corner of the sheet, poking out beneath a pile of cleaner titles. "I couldn't help but stare. Your dress is amazing. I can just make out the faint outline of your hips." I rolled my eyes as I sensed his flagrant bullshit comment. The dress I was wearing was hardly amazing; it was a simple yellow cotton tube dress that could be mistaken for a tunic because of its lack of length.

"Well, thank you for the compliment. It's one of my favorites," I smiled.

"So, I see you managed to find the porn selection. *Big Black Asses* is a favorite of mine." I would typically be turned off by the seedy nature I discerned in him, but I was somewhat intrigued by this man. There was something boldly seductive about him.

"Actually, I was not interested in the porn. I was looking for an indie flick to add to my private collection. Don't be so presumptuous."

"How about we grab something to eat, and then I can show you *my* private collection," he cajoled, licking his lips.

"How about you're a disgusting pervert, and you should get the fuck out of my face," I replied, matter-of-factly. He busted out laughing, and I laughed, too. It was a pretty abrasive response that could either come off as appealing, or a total turn-off. I prayed it was the latter.

"You know I'm just pulling your leg, right?" he laughed.

"Of course. Let's exchange numbers." I grinned a devilish smile. "And then maybe we can watch a bit of my private collection," I laughed. We dated for about a month, until he called me one night to meet him in Union Square to have sex in the park amongst the rats that played around the monument in the center of the park.

"Just meet me in the park. You don't have to wear any panties," I remember him cheerfully suggesting over the phone. I was revolted at the thought of fist-sized rats running over our feet as we fucked beside the bushes. I hadn't spoken to him since, and I thought he was all but a dead memory. So I wasn't exactly thrilled to see him that night on the L train platform, going in the same direction as I was going.

"You're still an asshole, I see," I scowled, wiping my lips.
He laughed confidently. "What have you been up to?" he asked.

"Oh, just traveling, working, dancing. You?"

"I actually just got back from Ethiopia. The women there are amazing."

I suddenly remembered why I hated this asshole. Not only did he have the audacity to outright kiss me without my permission, but he further felt the need to one-up me on his travel expeditions, AND let me know about the other, hotter women that he observed. He was cocky, brazen, and outspoken, when he could have benefited from a bit of silence. Besides, I remembered that he had an obsessive-compulsive disorder for cleanliness that caused him to shower after each bodily function. I shuddered at the memories of having to repeatedly wash my hands whenever I walked from one corner of his apartment to another.

"That's awesome" I replied, coolly. "I'm actually planning a trip to India for a month or so."

"India. Wow. I've always wanted to go there. We should go together!" He was excited and wide-eyed. I had my reservations because I really didn't want to go on a trip with an ex. Too much drama. It had become second nature for me to travel alone. But then again, I wasn't too sure about this excursion and thought that maybe it couldn't hurt to have a male travel mate with me.

"I'll think about it. I mean, I already made the plans." This was a lie. I had a rough itinerary at best. I didn't even have all of my money together for the trip.

"Okay, well give me a call. I think I still have your number. Let me check." He looked in his cell-phone book. I hoped he lost it. "917-361-2511, right?" I nodded in disappointment. Before I knew it, I was at my stop on Bedford Avenue, and I quickly waved and jumped off the train before he had the chance to repeat another sleazy stunt.

~

The feelings between my Abdoulaye and me were becoming increasingly strained, not only because of conflicting schedules, but more probably because of lack of interest. I wasn't taking class where he taught as much, because I really didn't want to be bothered with the awkwardness. I just wanted to dance. I ended up going to class, anywhere but the studio—Mark Morris, Alvin Ailey, The Harlem Y—anywhere. If I did take classes there, it was when he wasn't teaching, so that I wouldn't have to look at him. He disgusted and fascinated me at the same time, and my life had been uncomfortably absorbed in his realm of being. I wanted myself back, but I didn't know how to detach myself from him. So I bought plane tickets and traveled across the globe as a coping mechanism.

I became consumed with this India trip. I was excited, scared, and a little overwhelmed. What if things didn't work out? I was in the midst of planning my trip when Elijah called. I had willfully forgotten our run-in a few weeks earlier.

"Hey girl. So what's going on with India? I haven't heard from you!" I know, I thought. That's why I didn't call you.

"Oh, you know how it is. I work full-time, and I've just been so busy."

"Did you get your tickets yet?" I wanted to lie, but instead I blurted, "Yeah, I just went to my travel agent and picked them up. They were cheaper than anything I could find online. My flight is May fifteenth." I don't know what compelled me to give him all those details. Maybe it was my fear of truly going alone to a developing country where I didn't know any Hindi, let alone the hundreds of dialects therein.

"Oh, great! Well, I still want to go. What agent did you use?" I told him. Again, I could have kicked myself, and I quickly added that he probably shouldn't try to come.

"You know, India is really, really dirty. Are you sure you can cope?" I asked.

"Oh yeah, I can deal. I'll just bring my own cleaners, and I won't touch the people." This phrase alone should have sent me running, but instead I retreated.

"Okay, well. See you at JFK in two weeks." I prayed I would make it through this trip.

~

I arrived at JFK and headed straight for the Lufthansa check-in. Elijah was already there, standing in line. He was remarkably calm.

"Hey," I called out.

"Ah, you're actually late. I thought I would be the one late. I'm never on time." I was relieved at his self-deprecating comment. We checked our bags and headed for the gate, drama-free. The flight went smoothly as well, even with our stopover in Amsterdam. Maybe this wasn't going to be such a bad trip after all.

~

We arrived in the dead of night, and the heat and dust hit us like a brick wall. I had arranged for a taxi for us, and luckily, it was waiting for us at the gate. We made it to our hotel in about twenty minutes, and checked in. It was the shittiest hotel room I had ever been in. Surely the hookers in Atlantic City had better accommodations. The room was a dank eight-by-eight hole in the wall with off-white walls. There was a stained red carpet beneath us, and I didn't dare put my bags there. Instead, we lay our belongings on a pair of chairs. The bathroom was an unholy stall with a space in the corner with a faucet for a shower. Next to the shower was a toilet with a two-inch brown ring around the inside of the bowl. Eli and I stared at each other in disbelief. The Lonely

Planet guide listed this hotel as one of the better budget lodgings in New Delhi.

The sheets were covered in oil spots, and had a funky, musty smell. Everything had a coat of dust. The towels, which we vowed not to use, were a dingy white. We called the attendant and asked for fresh linen, and he returned with an equally dirty, equally oily set. I gave up, undressed, and put my dirty clothes on the bed. I didn't even want to lie there, but we had no choice. I would rather sleep on top of my dirty clothes than on the dirty sheets. There was no toilet paper, and the hotel wanted to charge us an unseemly fee. So, we ventured out into the night in search of toilet paper. I didn't know why Eli felt so confident until we left the hotel and he showed me a blade in the shape of a hawk's claw that he had neatly tucked into a pocket of his cargo pants. It was a horrific object, but for some reason, I felt safe knowing that he had something to protect us, just in case we ran into trouble.

Luckily we found a man selling toilet paper on the street for about forty rupees a roll. We bought several and headed back to the hotel. We really wanted to search out other hotels, but it was past midnight, so we figured we would make it through the night and book something new first thing in the morning. We were on our way back to the hotel when we suddenly heard a scuffle. A group of about five Indian men had surrounded a hapless white guy down the street. We stared at them, frozen as to what we should do. Eli had his blade, but he didn't want to use it. It was our first night in the country, and he surely didn't want to see the inside of an Indian jail cell. He had already done time on Rikers for assault with a deadly weapon. We both watched in horror as they dragged the hapless guy into an alley, and when they turned their heads away from us, we escaped back to our hotel room.

The following morning, I got up early. I wanted to get out of that awful hotel room and get some fresh air while Eli was asleep. Unfortunately, I wouldn't find it on the street where we were staying. The air was pungent with the scent of people, food, and animals. Because of a light rain the day before, the ground was muddy with red clay so that clumps of trash and animal shit filled the streets. The shops were lined stall-to-stall with clothing, jewelry, musical instruments, and toys so that there was not an inch to spare. I felt a bit overwhelmed with the abundance of sight and sound before me, and when I stood back to take it all in I nearly got ran over by a rickshaw. Every step I took, there was a honk or a shout, as cars, auto-rickshaws, and cow herders, hurled their frustrations at me. I found the nearest Internet café and wrote an e-mail to my mother.

FROM: sxybareftdncr@yahoo.com
TO: lvemyskn@yahoo.com
SUBJECT: We're in India!

Hi Mom. We just got to New Delhi last night. Our hotel is really crappy. We saw a mugging last night, but luckily Eli packed a hand blade. The city is pretty dirty, but there are so many shops and things to see. We will stay here for two days and then take a train to Agra to see the Taj Mahal. I'll mail you once we get there. xoxo

~

It was still early in the morning, so I decided to explore the shop-filled road. I picked up a cup of fresh chai from a street vendor, and popped in to some clothing shops where I found several pants and top sets called *salwar kameez*, which I planned to wear for my eagerly anticipated trip to the Taj Mahal. I lingered on and found some small pieces of jewelry and then headed back to the hotel to see if Eli was awake and dressed. I wanted to hurry up and check out of the hotel so that we could hopefully find a better, cheaper hotel in the area before leaving for Agra.

It was only ten-thirty a.m., but I felt like I had spent an entire day trying to navigate the dense street. Eli was in the shower doing an extensive bathing ritual, and after another forty-five minutes, he emerged, happily cleansed.

"I had to bathe off all of the filth from this room," he said disdainfully. "I can't wait to find another hotel. I hope all of India isn't this nasty." I actually agreed with him, even though I knew his aversion to dirt was an obsession. We finally left the place and spent the day scouring the city with all of our belongings. I would have settled on the first clean hotel that we discovered, but Eli was a perfectionist and insisted on finding the largest, cheapest room.

Walking around with a traveler's backpack, up and down steps, viewing trashy, overpriced hotels in hot, humid weather was not how I wanted to spend the little time I had in India.

Hot, sweaty, and annoyed, I wandered off to a vendor selling fresh mango lassis and settled down, away from the crazy streets. The shade of the vendor offered hardly any comfort as the 110° heat mixed the funk of the streets with the sugary smell of over-ripened mangoes. I watched as he sliced the fleshy mangoes and put them in a hand blender filled with ice. He then opened a large vat of chilled yogurt, poured a bit into a metal cup, and mixed in the blended fruit. Handing it to me, I told him that I wanted it to go, and he simply put the mixture in a plastic bag and sent me on my way. Beside me was a young white woman, tanned a deep olive tone. She wore a worn, yellow crochet halter-top and baggy green cargo pants, with a pair of well-worn leather sandals. She sat, cross-legged, staring into space as she sipped her lassi from one of the tin cups that all the locals seemed to use. She was completely at peace, and I wanted to experience that. I sat on a dirty bench not far from her to relax and take in the environment. I bit off the edge of the bag, and savored the icy sweetness of the treat. For one moment I was relaxed, happy, and careless. The pristine white dress I wore was now covered with street grime and the unidentified splashes from wild animals and pedi-rickshaws. I was ready to shower, and settle down. It was only noon.

We eventually found the hotel of Eli's dreams and settled down into our new space. I could finally bathe and relax a bit before exploring more of New Delhi and more importantly, get our train tickets to Agra. I wanted to get on the first train out of the city so that we would have plenty of time to enjoy the Taj Mahal. Eli and I walked down Main Bazaar Road, which was by now bustling with shop owners selling their wares to overwhelmed tourists. Children chased down prospective buyers and haggling could be heard in every direction. The shouting and singing, car honks and cow grunts, were a symphony of sensory overload. We nearly forgot that we needed to purchase our train tickets before the station closed.

~

We got to the New Delhi train station and were horrified to see the main floor of the station covered with sleeping Indian families, suitcases, chickens, and aggressive men pushing forward on a line where there was none. We glanced up to try and decipher the train lines and departures but were dismayed to find them all in Hindi! What to do! I finally pushed my way to the front of an information line and yelled, "Shatabdi Express!" The woman at the window directed me to a tourist room above the main lobby that could assist me in buying a ticket. Eli and I quickly made our way upstairs to the serenity of the Tourist Information Center, where there was no line, friendly staff, and air conditioning. We were well on our way to ordering our tickets until the ticket agent asked us to produce our passports. I had made it a point to carry all of my most important documents close to my body at all times in a discreet body pouch near my chest. No way would I be leaving my documents in some shady hotel. Eli left everything he had at the hotel except for his cash, which would not do in this situation. So we basically had to go back to our hotel at the opposite end of the Bazaar, get his documents, and come back to the station before seven-thirty. Given that we started off late and spent half the day looking at hotels and shopping, my mood wasn't exactly friendly. It was four p.m. Going back down Main Bazaar Road was an exercise in self-restraint. And when it comes to shopping, I have absolutely none. So I ended up purchasing a bunch of shirts, shoes, and . . . so many things, I can't even remember! When we finally got back to the hotel, it was nearly six p.m., and we had little time before the ticket window closed. So, we hopped into our first rickshaw, but not until Eli had haggled with twenty or so drivers for the best price. We arrived at the station with fifteen minutes to spare.

~

The next morning I woke up early and was packed and ready to go before Eli even blinked an eye. Because this new hotel room was bigger and cleaner, Eli had decided to become comfortable and unpack every single one of his belongings. Eli had brought his portable game console, his iPod, and a laptop just in case he got bored. His iPod was charging in an expensive dock with Bose speakers. He had even taken the time to display the bits of trash and snacks that he had stashed from the flight, just in case he ran out of food. I sat looking at all of his shit scattered around the room and wondered how we would possibly make the train in time.

"Eli!" I shouted. "Can you get up? We have to go!" He shuffled a bit on his side of the bed.

"Well look at you, all chipper in the morning!"

"Our train is at eight a.m. and it's already six. Can you get up and get ready? I know how long you take to get yourself situated." He huffed and dragged himself out of the bed to begin his cleaning ritual. By the time he was ready, I had already checked out of the hotel and was waiting in the taxi, ready to go.

~

We were intending to take the first train out of New Delhi to Agra. I wanted to get there early, so that we would have time to get a bite to eat, freshen up, and really take our time looking at the Taj Mahal, but leave it to Eli to be late. Once again, we got to the train station and were flanked by several livestock and hungry children hoping for a coin or two for a meal. I opened my wallet, filled with rupees and some American coins.

We boarded the Shatabdi Express, where we sat in comfort, for our three-hour-long train ride. The car was air conditioned, clean, and well organized. Food arrived for us in steady increments, and we had a pleasant conversation with our cabin mates. It would be our last luxury transport for a while.

It was around eleven a.m. when we arrived in Agra, and I honestly didn't know what to do. Since Eli was relying on my navigation skills, he was useless. We found a friendly cab driver who took us around the city before finally dropping us off at what was to be our lodging. After what we had experienced in New Delhi, we weren't about to settle for another crappy hotel, so we scrapped our reservations and went in search of better lodging. Even though I was exhausted, Eli insisted on looking at every hotel on the block. There didn't seem to be any hotel that was large enough, or clean enough. After poking around for nearly an hour we settled on a nearby inn that was suggested by our driver, Sam. Because of his helpfulness, we decided to hire him for the rest of the day as our driver, the cost being so little between us. He agreed to wait for us as we checked in, unloaded our bags, and showered. The porter guided us to a room on the second level of the hotel. The rooms were spaced around a central patio, where visitors could sit out on the shielded veranda and have a cup of tea while observing the landscape. Our room was a clean, windowless box on the far side of the open space. The porter gave us our keys and left us to unpack.

"I don't like this room. Why don't we try to find a room with a view of the Taj Mahal?" Eli asked.

"Why didn't you ask before we started unpacking? I have all my shit out and I'm ready to lie down, and now you want to change rooms?" I was annoyed, but Eli had already walked out of the door down to the front desk to change rooms. The porter came back upstairs and led us to another, slightly larger room with three windows, one of which offered an obscure view of the Taj Mahal. I had to admit that the room was brighter and a little cozier, with colorful throw pillows and a small mirror-embellished coffee table and chairs that brightened the room.

"You see? Eli scolded. "You'll never know what you're missing out on if you don't ask. Oh, and since I found the room, I get first dibs on the shower." I agreed and grudgingly repacked my bag to move to the new room.

While he showered, I turned over on the bed and looked out of the window at the Taj Mahal. It was so white and serene against the startling blue sky. The way the varying hues of purple-orange sunset bounced off its dome created an enchanting halo effect that could never be captured in a postcard. I was still shocked that I had actually made it here.

I stripped naked and waited to take my shower. At this point, I was so sweaty, sticky, and smelly from our journey, I didn't care if Eli had the chance to stare at my naked body. My feelings toward him were more of an annoying brother type than a past lover with whom I might rekindle a love affair. Eli got out of the shower and came into the main room, completely nude and dripping with water. I looked at his naked, glistening, muscular body from the bed, and though I had the perfect chance, the truth was, I wouldn't fuck him with a hazmat suit on. He had three kids from three different women, and he was reckless with his affairs and his choice of words. These crazy, narcissistic, masochistic types seemed to always fall into my realm. I guess I was a sadist.

He stood there rubbing his body with shea butter, preening in the center of the room as the fading sunlight bounced off his muscles. I found myself slightly aroused but then remembered all the reasons why it would never work. I stared at him for a moment longer and then shook my head and walked off into the shower. No sooner had I turned on the water than I heard Sam shouting from the floor below.

"Hello! Hello! Let's go! No Time!"

"We're coming!" Eli and I shouted simultaneously. Because Eli spent most of the time we had bathing himself and getting ready, I had no time for myself. I quickly showered and dressed before heading downstairs into Sam's cab.

Sam took us around the town to every place except the Taj Mahal. We drove past the Baby Taj, and around Agra Fort, though we never entered these places because of the additional fee. By the time we were ready for lunch, Sam had already preselected a restaurant for us, but we had caught on to his ploy. He basically took us to where his accomplices worked so that they could try to sell us their wares.

Eli was annoyed by the ruse because the restaurants Sam was picking were clearly not vegetarian. At one point Eli got out of the car and just walked to the restaurant of his choice, leaving a frustrated Sam to sulk alone in his car. When we were finished eating, I asked Sam to bring us to a postal office where we could find out about shipping some of our wares back home. Shopping in New Delhi had been a bonanza, and Eli and I had racked up a small collection of Indian wares that were sure to accumulate as our trip wore on. But instead of a legit post office, Sam brought us to a friend's embroidery shop, who volunteered to sew our belongings into a packet and ship them back to the States for an exorbitant fee. We passed on that idea and just resolved to pay the extra baggage fee at the airport. Again, Sam was gypped of a commission, and stomped off to his rickshaw.

"Sam, I want to get a massage. Can you recommend anyplace good?" I knew he already had someone in mind, and he quickly whisked us away to a small storefront where about five massage therapists awaited new customers.

"I want a massage!" Eli exclaimed. "It must be dirt cheap. I want the women massaging me." Just then, the head proprietor approached us.

"I'm sorry sir, but it is custom for women to massage only women. If you want a massage, I can offer you one."

"Oh hell no, I'm not getting massaged by a dude. Women give the massages back home." I laughed and rolled my eyes at Eli as I strolled inside to receive my deep-tissue massage and hot-stone therapy treatment. The cost was a relative song, and I emerged relaxed and rejuvenated to the annoyance of Eli.

"Let's go," he huffed. "I'm tired."

It was the end of our day. We were beat, and we looked forward to a comfortable ride back to the hotel. Sam was watching his cricket game at a fabric shop next door to the masseuse, and when he saw us approach his rickshaw he waved us away.

"No, no, you can go to your hotel. Easy! Very Easy! Take this road . . ." My jaw dropped in the shadow of the deepening sunset. "Wait, are you telling us to walk back to our hotel?" I asked, shocked at the notion.

"Safe! Very safe!" Sam exclaimed. "Very easy!" he shouted as he pointed down the road. Eli laughed as we watched Sam hop into his rickshaw and speed off into the night, leaving us in a cloud of dust.

"Hey, it can't be too hard," Eli reasoned. And it's still a little light out. I have my knife and my flashlight with me. It should be fine."

After about walking for an hour, amazingly we made it back to the hotel unscathed. Before reaching the hotel, we stopped at a vendor offering fresh chai in what seemed to be the town square behind the Taj Mahal. We watched as children played with scraps in the mud and excited locals cheered at the cricket game being broadcast out of tinny television sets. The night was pleasantly warm, and we walked around for a bit before retiring to bed.

~

It may have been two a.m. when I woke to a drip on my

face. Half asleep, I rolled over toward Eli, half-awake, in a sort of dream state. Another few drips fell on my shoulder and I slid closer to him subconsciously as the drips followed me. Then the random sound of drips could be heard on his side of the bed. Eli popped his head up suddenly.

"Water! It's . . . raining! In. . . the room!" I stuttered, half-awake. When our minds finally deciphered what was happening, we immediately jumped out of our bed before the ceiling came crashing down with rain! Outside, we could hear the winds whistling as torrential rains surrounded the building. We quickly moved our belongings toward the door, and flipped the light switch. And then the lights went out in the village. We could hear the staff's footsteps as they brought up battery-powered florescent lights to help us see. Outside of our rooms you could hear the cries of people who had likely slept outside and gotten caught in the storm. Who would have known it would rain? It was as hot and arid as it could be that day! We eventually moved our stuff back to the original room we were given, and I silently cursed Eli for being so damn picky. But I slept soundly, eager for the Taj at sunrise.

~

I woke up early to have a cup of chai and try to catch the Taj Mahal in an early sunlit glow. Eli was in a blissful slumber, and I relished the chance to be alone on the veranda to enjoy the peacefulness of the early morning. The sky was overcast, and though I tried to get a good shot of the monument, its pristine white tiles were dulled against the gray clouds.

I heard footsteps behind me while I was busy snapping pictures.

"Why didn't you wake me? I wanted to take pictures, too."

"Oh, I didn't want to bother you. You were in a deep sleep." Eli glanced at me with a side-eye. "Whatever. So when are we going to the Taj Mahal?"

"It seems really overcast right now. Why don't we go and get our tickets and then go back in the afternoon when the sun comes out?"

"Sounds like a plan."

~

We got dressed and walked over to the building early to avoid the crowds. Luckily, it was only a five-minute walk away from the hotel because when we arrived at the gate it started to lightly drizzle. We purchased our entrance tickets and headed back to the hotel to sleep it out in hopes of a sunnier view later on in the day. On our way back we noticed several young boys selling batteries, candies, and trinkets to the scores of visitors that streamed in and out of the monument. One of the boys came up to us to offer some batteries.

"No thank you," I waved to the boy, with a smile. He kept walking beside us, trying hard to sell us on something. "No, I don't need anything, thanks."

"How do you like my country?" the boy asked, eagerly.

"I love the country, but your people are nasty," Eli stated flatly. The boy looked on, unfazed. I wanted to slap Eli across the Atlantic.

"You know, that was a really shitty thing to say."

"How is it shitty, to be honest about things?"

"It's a thing called tact. If you had it, then people wouldn't think you were such an asshole."

He rolled his eyes, as if I were the one being unreasonable. I quickened my pace so that I ended up walking a few steps ahead of him. I really didn't want to be associated with this pompous idiot. When I got back to the hotel, I retreated to the veranda with a book and a cup of chai while Eli went back to sleep.

~

Several hours later, the sun had barely peeked past the clouds. We decided to take our chances and go to the Taj anyway since we were due to leave the following morning. We found the gate to the Taj, and walked in. Two female security guards checked our bags for contraband. Eli was wise enough not to bring his knives this time, or he wouldn't have been let in. As we walked through the gates, he hopped around like a monkey.

"Take my picture!" He whipped out his camera and fixed his locs. I snapped a postcard-perfect picture. "Take another one. Wait, let me fix my hair." I rolled my eyes. "Okay, now." He preened and smiled, and posed like a peacock. I tried to hide my embarrassment as tons of native Indians passed us, gawking, pointing, and laughing. I heard some of them remark that we were Africans. Several children ran up to me, and asked if I would take a picture with them, while most other passersby simply took our photo without asking. What started off as a funny experience quickly turned annoying as hordes of Indian tourists began flanking us and filming our every move as we tried to enjoy the monument in peace. After about an hour spent making a spectacle of ourselves, we had had enough and went back to the hotel to relax.

Back at the hotel, I took some time to drink a little chai, read, have a late breakfast, and chat with the staff. As I showered, I could hear Eli getting frustrated as he tore through his bags.

"What the fuck?" he screamed.

"What's wrong now?" I screamed past the shower door. But by then, Eli had already stormed downstairs to the front desk.

"Where's my fucking money, man? Was there someone in our room?" he screamed with an anger that could be heard throughout the hotel. Eli had thought it was genius to leave a wad of folded bills under the mattress and now he couldn't find the stashed money. The manager came out and pointed to the young boy who had been cleaning the rooms.

"I assure you," the manager pleaded, "Nobody took your money."

"That's some bullshit. I know where I left my money. If I

don't get my money back, somebody's getting their ass kicked, for real. Where is my FUCKING MONEY, MAN?" By then Eli had attracted all of the hotel staff as well as a few other guests. I quickly got dressed so as to not be caught off-guard when the parade of onlookers came into our room.

"I left my money right here," Eli pointed. The hapless boy shrugged his shoulders.

"Okay, y'all are fuckin' playing now. Somebody knows what happened to my money." Eli moved toward the young boy but the manager stepped in to intervene.

"Now, now, we don't need to get physical." He spoke to the boy in a Hindi dialect. "He says that he doesn't know".

"Listen man, if you don't get me my fucking money, I swear, I'm gonna have someone do some voodoo on your ass. Do you know what voodoo is?" He pronounced the word slowly and loudly, like he was talking to a toddler. "It makes you go all crazy and shit. I know people!" I didn't know whether to be incredibly horrified of Eli's raging antics or to laugh at Eli's enunciation of the word.

"Eli, why don't we go and get something to eat, and we can retrace your steps. I'm sure the money's in one of your pockets or something." The hotel staff agreed, and I'm sure they were relieved as we left the hotel for the night.

"Those poor ass Indians. They know they took my shit. You know they took my shit!"

"No, I don't Eli. Be rational." We found a small diner offering simple Masalas and dosas and ate in relative silence.

"When I get back, my money better be there, or all hell is gonna break loose. And I really don't want to go to jail again."

~

We returned to the hotel room and Eli found his money neatly tucked under the mattress on his side of the bed. Relieved, we got ready for the following day's departure, and slept peacefully through the night.

Our trip continued the following morning. The train from Agra to Jaipur was not as luxurious as the one from New Delhi to Agra. The change in transportation was likely due to the popularity of the Taj Mahal as a premier tourist destination. Our Jaipur train was run down and cramped, even though we had chosen the supposed first-class seats. We met a group of American college students who happened to share the same car with us. We noticed that people from the same country had been grouped together, likely as a safeguard and reassurance for the travelers. Our seat was one row in front of the toilets and when I went to go use the bathroom, I was appalled by the rancid hole, covered in urine and feces.

We arrived in Jaipur at around ten p.m. and luckily, I had picked one of the best budget hotels in the area. The rooms were ample-sized, clean, and colorfully painted. Each room had an elaborate wood-carved door that I found incredibly charming. But of course Eli could not be satisfied when we were shown our room.

"Eli, it's late, what's wrong with this room?"

"We may find something better." I thought about our disastrous event in Agra as I dropped my bags in the room.
The weary owner took us to another, larger room. Inside, there was an air conditioner, and a huge bright light bulb in the center of the ceiling that seemed to illuminate the whole street.

"See? This room is much better! It's bigger, brighter. It's only two hundred rupees more per night. We might as well splurge."

"No, I was happy with the other one. It's just what we need. Plus, I don't intend on staying in the hotel room all that much. And I don't trust your judgment considering what happened to us in Agra." He grudgingly picked up his bags and moved back to our original room. That night, I tried to plan the following day's activities since Eli had never bothered to research anything about the country, let alone glance at the Loney Planet guidebook. I found a slew of vegetarian restaurants that would appeal to both of us, as well as a jeweler and a short mountain climb to the Monkey Temple at the end of the day. We would have dinner at Om, the rotating restaurant towering above the Old Pink City, an area of town where the walls were constructed of pink stone.

"What do you think?"

"It all sounds good. I trust you'll find something interesting for us to do. But the Monkey Temple sounds real good. I wanna do that." He rolled over and went to sleep like a happy little boy. I quickly jotted down the day's events and crawled into bed.

~

The following day I woke up early to get a head start on a shower and breakfast before Eli would have the chance to annoy me. I quickly bathed and grabbed a few wrinkled clothes that desperately needed ironing. When I stepped out of our room, the blazing sunlight hit my body, and engulfed me in such a pleasing warmth that I smiled.

In the daylight, I finally got to take in the charming nature of the hotel. It was more along the lines of a bed and breakfast, quietly tucked amongst residential houses on an off-road. The wooden doors of each hotel room were intricately carved in traditional Indian aesthetic, and I marveled at how they seamlessly fit in with the architecture of the otherwise simple hotel. The walls of each room were colored a cheerful hue, with shades of yellow, purple, and blue filling the residence. I had made it a point to book at least one night in a hotel from the previous city, so that we would at least have a place to stay for the first night. So far, that plan had been disastrous, as all of my bookings had been far short of what their Internet descriptions had depicted. This cheap little hotel, in the center of Jaipur was such a far departure from the filthy, dim-lit rooms we had experienced in New Delhi.

"This is a wonderful place," I remarked to the innkeeper. He smiled at me. "How did you find out about us?" He mentioned a popular American guidebook.

"From an Internet forum. I will never use that book again, and I'm going to write to those people about false advertising." The truth of the matter was that Eli and I had been finding better, cheaper deals on hotels on our own than with the ten-pound book I had purchased in Barnes & Noble just before my trip. The owner glanced at the bundle of clothes in my hand.

"Laundry?"

"Oh no, I actually washed these last night. I just wanted to get them ironed. Do you have any recommendations?" He suggested that I look around for a local launderer who would likely iron my clothing for a pittance, and I made my way outside to explore the neighborhood.

The streets were filled with locals going about their business, looking for any way to generate income. Children ran, barefoot and dirty, carelessly jumping over broken glass and cow dung. Beyond their appearance I saw the faces of happy children, full of life, curiosity, and excitement. They saw me and immediately crowded around offering their grubby hands for a handshake. I hugged them and greeted them in an uncomplicated display of affection.

I came back to the hotel room to find Eli lying in corpse pose under a thin sheet. I noticed that he had gotten up to connect his iPod to his sophisticated speaker dock, and was listening to a young girls' choir singing in Hindi.

"What are you doing?" I asked. Eli jumped, startled at the

sound of my voice, which cut harshly over the soothing sounds of the voices. I stood there, looking at the fool lying there with his eyes closed, in a reflective state.

"I'm meditating."

"You do know that there's an ashram down the street. It's inside a girl's prep school. We are in India, just in case you forgot."

"Really?" he asked, genuinely perplexed. This guy was more of an idiot than I thought.

"Listen, I want to get a good head start on the day. I just went out and got my clothes ironed. I'm gonna go and check my e-mail and try to find an inexpensive hotel for our next stop in Goa. I guess when we get back we can head out." I went down-stairs to the innkeeper, where he allowed me to check my e-mail from one of his old desktop computers.

"Where will you be going today?"

"We were thinking of exploring the Old Pink City. I liked the story of the different merchants being divided by block."

"That's great. But I must warn you. There were some bombings here not too long ago. You won't see many tourists around, but it's generally safe."

"I'm sure we'll be fine. We'd also like to go to the Monkey Temple. Do you know of the place?"

"Ah yes, it's on top of a hill, and there is a small temple on top where you can see the entire city. It's a wonderful place to view the sunset. Maybe you can get a blessing while you're up there."

"I need as many blessings as I can get. My partner is driving me crazy."

"I can tell," he laughed. "Good luck with that."

~

Eli was invigorated from his faux meditation and he was eager to explore the Old Pink City as one of the few tourists. Luckily we had missed the terrorist bombings a few weeks prior that had damaged parts of the historic town, and scared most of the foreign tourists away. "More opportunities for us," he said as a swarm of rickshaw operators surrounded us. "We can give them anything and they'll take us. We're the only ones with money."

"Eli, that's fucked up. Just because we are at an advantage doesn't mean that we have to exploit the locals. You have no ethics." Eli shrugged and waved for a rickshaw. About ten guys pedaled around us.

"Listen," he said to the crowd, "We wanna go to the center of the city. How much?"

"Thirty rupees!" shouted one driver.

"Twenty-five rupees!" shouted another.

"Twenty rupees!" shouted a third.

"I will take you for ten rupees!" a skinny young man called out from behind the group. They all turned and looked at him incredulously.

"Ten rupees?" they all gasped, angry at the undercut price.

They shook their heads. Eli folded his arms in amusement as he watched the drivers quarrel over the price.

"Eight rupees." Eli smiled a shit-eating grin. I was shocked and stared at him with my mouth agape.

"Eli, that is larceny. What is eight rupees to you? It's nothing! Come on."

"It's supply and demand," he replied, nonchalantly. He turned back to the lowest bidder. "How is eight rupees?" The driver nodded and we got into the cab.

"I'm gonna give him extra."

"For what? You know, I was gonna suggest five rupees, but I took you into consideration."

"How thoughtful," I replied as I watched him gaze at the atmosphere of the city, his body half-stuck out of the rickety pedal cab. When Eli wasn't looking, I slipped the driver ten rupees. We eventually made it to what was more or less the city center, and we got out to grab lunch at a vegetarian restaurant recommended by the Lonely Planet guide. Eli paid the driver the promised eight rupees and hopped out of the rickshaw. The streets were teeming with pedicabs, vendors, and homeless people hawking whatever they could find to sell. I was overwhelmed with the sheer amount of locals that flooded us wherever we went.

"I want to go to the jewelry section in the Old Pink City. I'm looking for some pure gold," Eli said, mesmerized.

"I don't mind looking, but are you prepared to lay down that type of cash? I thought you were light on funds?"

"Yeah, but if the piece is right, I won't need to buy anything else." I rolled my eyes at his foolishness and walked into the restaurant. The mood was quiet and somber as the intimate tables sat eerily empty. There was an Indian businessman and his partner seated nearby eating an abundant, luxurious meal with wine. They were clearly not a part of the local demographics as they happily flashed their wealth at us obvious Americans.

My dish came out first and I luxuriated over the wondrous array of colors, flavors, and spices it contained. Our table was filled with of sumptuous Indian food. The tangy, sweet spices of the sauces and vegetables popped in my mouth, and I nearly doubled over from the taste of the intense flavors. I nearly forgot about Eli as I ate my lunch.

"What are you ordering?" I asked after-the-fact.

"Everything looks great. I want it all. It's vegetarian. I'm sure there are plenty of vegan dishes." A waiter standing nearby overheard my comments.

"Actually, if you want vegan, you can only order the dosas," the waiter stated.

"Really? But I've been eating vegetable dishes since we got here," Eli answered.

"They all use ghee, an oil derived from goats that was is in all the local dishes."

"So I've been eating animal by-product all this time?" Eli asked in despair. I laughed evilly inside. "Well, now you know," I said matter-of-factly, scarfing down my meal. Eli sat at the table, unsettled by the revelation. The waiter brought out his meal, and he cautiously picked at it until I was ready to go.

~

We decided to take our chances and walk to the Old Pink City because we wanted to see what was in the streets, and maybe find a bargain or two. We walked freely, and the locals gawked at us, as we not only were obviously tourists, but black tourists as well. I'm sure everyone assumed we were American, and it didn't help that Eli made crass comments at every passerby in his heavy Harlemite accent.

"Do you ever have anything nice to say? Your mouth is gonna get you into a lot of trouble."

He brushed me off. "Please. Anybody touches me and I'll slay them. Don't forget—I'm a jiu jitsu master." He walked ahead of me with his chest out. His boisterous attitude was turning me off, and I tried hard not to be seen with him as we approached more crowds of shoppers. On each side of us were rows upon rows of shops, neatly tucked away inside the pink stone walls, where delicate treasures could be found and had for the right price. I listened to the bustle as eager shopkeepers hustled their wares to a crowd hesitant to part with their money.

Eli was definitely on the hunt for a precious gold necklace. He ran from booth to booth, examining rare jewels and intricate-ly-designed costume pieces. While he looked for jewelry, I sat with a group of working-class men who had gathered around a man who was making fresh lime and cane juice. I bought a cup and reveled in its sweet tanginess.

"Hey! Look at this," Eli called to me. He ducked inside a booth filled with textiles and linen of all colors, extravagantly embroidered with sequins and beads. I gasped at their beauty.

"These are stunning! I have to have one," I gasped in awe.

"How much?" Eli asked. The vendor gave him a price. "Oh, that's too much. I'll give you half that. They haggled for about fifteen minutes, with Eli threatening to go to another vendor. The beauty of the beautiful magenta blanket embroidered with sequined elephants mesmerized me. This type of extraordinary piece could easily sell for hundreds of dollars if I brought it to New York, though I had every intention of keeping it for myself.

"I have twenty-five in cash. How's that?" I asked the vendor. It was already a bargain from the price he had quoted me, which was over twice as much. The vendor happily accepted, but Eli would not budge. The two men stood, quarreling until the weary vendor settled for what would be fifteen dollars.

"You see," grinned Eli. "You don't know how to haggle."

"I disagree Eli. This blanket could easily go for two or three hundred dollars in America. I already got a bargain." I loved a bargain as much as he did, but I didn't enjoy undercutting a craftsman to the point of humiliation.

"If you say so," he shrugged.

~

We walked through the Old Pink City and tried to blend in with the robust energy that filled the streets. Open-air markets lined the cluttered roadways with richly embroidered linens and small, delicate handicrafts. Before long it was nighttime and we wanted to get to the top of the Monkey Temple to watch the sun set over the city of Jaipur. We took a pedicab to the edge of town where we would climb a steep hill to reach the shrine at the mountain's peak. Eli immediately began snapping pictures of the little children who ran around the base of the mountain, covered in dusty red clay. I watched as mothers sat contentedly among their children, conversing and enjoying the evening sun, and caught off-guard by Eli's flashing camera.

"Eli, can you just chill?" I asked, embarrassed.

"Don't worry, I'll pay them!" He handed a small girl with deep brown eyes a one hundred-rupee note, which was shocking, considering that he couldn't be bothered to fairly compensate a rickshaw driver.

"That's not the point. Don't you have any ethics? Just let them be!" I quickly walked off, climbing the mountain alongside goats and playful monkeys that ran between my legs at every turn. When I finally made it to the top, I saw a small temple in the center of the peak, with a single woman inside. She was blessing the altar, then turned and smiled at me when I entered.

The place seemed magical, with a few candles burning

near a statue of a goddess wrapped in flowers. The woman approached me and placed her thumb on my forehead, leaving a yellow ochre mark in its center. She then wrapped a pink string around my wrist, and waved as she left the temple. I left a few coins at the base of the statue and went back outside to find Eli doing a headstand, shirtless at the base of the mountain. Luckily there was a stone barrier around the mountain peak that kept visitors from falling off the ledge, but Eli was hell-bent on getting the perfect yoga pose for his archives. He climbed up on the ledge and sat Indian style.

"Take my picture!" I rolled my eyes, and grabbed his camera to take a shot. Then he decided to get a little more creative and do a frog pose on the tiny ledge.

"Are you sure you want to do that? It's a long fall to the bottom. I doubt you'd survive and even if you did, you probably wouldn't want to." He attempted the pose, and when his hand faltered, he used his better judgment for once, and got down.

"I'll just do some yoga over there," he said as he walked to the other corner of the mountain peak. I was relieved to get a few moments away from Eli. He was boisterous, overly confident, and loud—a complete manifestation of what foreigners likely believe Americans to be. I sat in a small space gazing at the darkening sky, colored with fantastic strokes of deep orange and purple. I took a deep breath, and closed my eyes, waiting for that special moment, that epiphany, the enlightenment that I had seen and read about so many times. After about twenty minutes, the moment never came.

"I'm hungry," I shouted to Eli. "Let's get to the restaurant so that we can get a good seat. I heard it gets pretty crowded."

"But I was just getting into my yoga poses," he whined. I glared back at him with a look that let him know that I knew he was full of shit. "All right, if you say so. I'm actually a little hungry, too." By the time we made it back down the hill, the sun had fully set and we were now in the midst of the monkeys and goats that followed us, and the city lights shone onto the glistening nostrils of the animals. We hailed a regular cab into the center of the city, where we would go to the famous rotating Shanti Restaurant. It wasn't a minute too soon before it began to rain, and when we stepped inside the doors of the fanciful eatery, it began to pour mercilessly.

The server greeted us and led us to the topmost level, where we observed a large family enjoying a birthday celebration. As I stepped to sit inside our booth, the floor rotated, and I quickly stepped my other foot onto solid ground where the table lay.

"This should be interesting," I thought as I glanced outside the booth's window at the city, which was now covered in a drizzling rain. We sat down, and I continued to gaze at the washed-out streets, lit only by the headlights of the automobiles. Our waiter arrived and we ordered our dishes with the expertise that we learned about at our lunchtime restaurant in the city center. Our food arrived in a dazzling display, and I took the time to document our cuisine taking several pictures. The waiter, noticing this, took it upon himself to further introduce himself and poke and prod around our dinner plates to describe the dishes. Eli looked on with disgust as the man poked his finger into ball-shaped pieces of dough covered in a sweet tamarind glaze.

"Well I don't know about you, but I wouldn't eat that. He felt all up on your shit."

For once, I agreed with Eli. I avoided that part of the dish and enjoyed the rest as we rotated slowly in our seats until we had viewed all of Jaipur. By the time we had finished our meal, it was nearly ten p.m. and the sky had opened up again and created a nasty rainstorm that caused the red clay soil to cake up around the wheels of all the cars stuck in traffic. We paid our bill and ran outside in the storm to take the first available cab back to the hotel.

~

"Boy, I'm exhausted," Eli yawned.

"Me too." I stripped down to my underwear, and sat down comfortably on a chair just outside the bathroom to begin jotting down the day's events. Eli did his pre-bed ritual and then climbed into the bed under the covers. Two minutes passed before Eli began to shuffle around discontentedly.

"But I want to sleep NOW!" Eli huffed childishly. He reminded me of the spoiled little girl from Charlie and the Chocolate Factory. Eli was definitely a rotten egg.

"What is the problem? Just go to sleep! I just need a few minutes to quickly write down some notes. I won't be long. Five minutes max." I went into the bathroom and shut the door, quickly writing my notes on the toilet.

"I can see the light coming from under the door, and it's distracting. I can't sleep with any lights on."
I rolled my eyes and walked out of the bathroom to sit on the chair. I left the door slightly ajar so that a sliver of light streamed from the crevice. "Are you fucking serious right now? Calm down!" I hissed. He huffed loudly.

"Can you *pleeaaase* turn the light out?" I ignored him. "Turn the fucking light off, I can't sleep!" I looked up and he was standing on the bed now, his arms folded in protest.

"What the hell is wrong with you? The room is pitch black, and the bathroom door is open to the tiniest slit. There is barely any light coming through."

"I can't sleep with any light. Why don't you go outside and sit in the courtyard?"

"Because I want to sit in the room that I paid for, in privacy. I'll be done in less than two minutes! Stop being such a drama queen!" I hissed as I finished writing the entry in my notebook. I signed off, shut the light, and went to bed, with violent thoughts of mashing his head into a chickpea sauce.

~

Eli woke up the following morning, moaning and grabbing his stomach.

"I feel like shit. There must have been something in that food." I nodded.

"Yeah, I just spent like twenty minutes on the toilet."

"Well, I can smell it. Whatever was in you isn't there any-more." He hopped out of the bed and ran to the bathroom to vomit. I felt a bit sorry for him, but another part of me reveled with glee at the payback that Mother Nature was playing on this ass-hat's stomach.

"Hopefully you can get it out of your system before we get to Goa. Hey, I was heading over to that ashram down the street. It's the one that's inside the girl's school."

"Nah, I'm not feeling up to it. I'll just lay here and hope-fully I'll feel better before we have to leave." I left him alone in the room to writhe in misery and relished the freedom of exploring the city without him. I didn't want to go too far because we had an afternoon flight to Goa and had arranged a cab to take us to the airport. I stopped by the owner's office to use the Internet.

"Did you enjoy your stay here?"

"Oh yeah, it was great. Well, up until this morning. I think we got food poisoning from the Shanti Restaurant. My partner is in the room, sick."

"Oh, that's too bad. Didn't you say you were flying to Goa today? If he's too sick, I don't think they'll let him board."

"I don't think it's that bad. He's a real drama queen. He probably just needs to go to the bathroom and then he'll be fine. I sat down at a computer and opened my e-mail.

FROM: drumdancelife@yahoo.com
TO: sxybrftdancer@yahoo.com
SUBJECT: Need your help

I flag it for follow-up and try to move on to the next message, but the inevitable curiosity creeps up on me. What could he possibly want? We hadn't been speaking regularly since before I had left for Brazil, and the conversations were tense. I had no real desire to be with someone who was suffocating, all-consuming, and emotionally unavailable. He was a selfish son of a bitch who not only demanded all of my time, but craved my attention, even though he had the hearts of tens of other women. I opened it.

Need a lead on a performance space for cheap or free.
-A

Not even a hello? Fuck that. He could get it from some other chick he was screwing. He was never pressed for willing volunteers so I'm sure he would have no trouble in finding whatever he needed. I clicked delete and moved to the next message, which was from my mother, asking how things were going.

TO: sxybareftdncr@yahoo.com
FROM: lvemyskn@yahoo.com
SUBJECT: hi

Hi pookie,

I just wanted to know how your trip was going. Where are you now? Keep me posted.

Love, Mom

TO: lvemyskn@yahoo.com
FROM: sxybareftdncr@yahoo.com
SUBJECT: Re: hi

Hi Mom,

Eli is a pain. He has been so disrespectful to everyone we have met and it's just annoying. Our hotel here in Jaipur is very quaint, cheap, and best of all, clean. We went to this fancy rotating restaurant in the center of the city that was written up in the Lonely Planet travel guide. It sounded really good and the food wasn't that bad. But I think we got food poisoning. Eli is in the room now with a horrible stomachache. We're still going to Goa this afternoon. I can't let him ruin our trip.

Love you.

I left the manager's office to have a cup of chai and walk around the neighborhood. An hour later, I returned and checked my email again. I was so desperate for any amount of reliable, sane interaction that I was checking my email more and more frequently those days. I had hoped that my mother would respond to my email, despite the time difference. Amazingly, she did.

TO: sxybareftdncr@yahoo.com
FROM: lvemyskn@yahoo.com
SUBJECT: Re: Re: hi

Hi baby,
I'm sorry Eli is being annoying. Most men are pussies and can't deal with pain anyway. He'll be fine. I'm praying for you.

Mommy

~

I walked around for a bit, grabbed a few trinkets and some bottled water, and returned to the hotel where Eli was still laying, in death pose, this time without music. He was sweating profusely and moaned when he saw me.

"I take it you're not feeling any better. You know what I think? Maybe we've been in too many dusty cities. You might do better on the beach in the south where there is plenty of open space and lots of plant life." Even I was longing for a bit of natural surroundings as the density, sights, and smells began to feel overwhelming to me.

"We have to get to Goa," I urged. Eli agreed, and we

packed our things before heading to the airport for our flight.

~

The drive from the airport to the southernmost beach in Goa took about an hour. With Eli slung over in the backseat, I asked the driver to take us around a few hotels so that I could find one that would suit us best. Without Eli and his big mouth in the way, I was able to find bright, clean, affordable accommodations quickly. The driver helped me bring in our luggage, while Eli dragged himself onto the bed, moaning in agony. I approached the owners and asked them what I should do for his sick stomach.

"Tell him to gargle with salt water, or better yet, a concoction of salt water and 7-Up." I ventured out to the nearest storefront along the path to the beach for a can of soda and a box of salt. The sun was absolutely delightful, and the breeze floated through the air, so that I could smell a mixture of saltwater and fresh food being prepared on open woks by the seaside. I purchased the goods and returned to our room. By now, Eli was puking all over the place. I gave him the mixture and left him to wallow in his misery while I went to the beach. Karma really is a bitch, I thought.

I changed into a full-piece suit, slathered on some sunscreen, and made my way down to the beach. Along the way were several shops and restaurants catering to a European tourist crowd. Lucky for us, we landed in Goa on the tail end of the height of tourist season, so there weren't too many foreign faces, and the prices were more relaxed. There was a brick-oven pizza place on the main strip, and I grabbed a personal pizza and a Coke. I loved the native Indian food, but I was craving something familiar.

Finally, I arrived on the beach and removed my sarong to lie down. If there was any place that I could lay near-nude it was Goa—or so I thought. I saw a few white tourists walking around in bikini tops and shorts, so I figured I was in the clear. No sooner had I sat down and began reading my novel than I could hear whistles and catcalls. I looked up and there were a pair of teenage Indian boys filming me with their video camera. I tried to shoo them away, but they just scurried to another area of the beach, all the while filming. I decided to wrap my sarong around my waist and try to relax again. Moments later, I could feel the breath and presence of someone standing over me. I shielded my face from the sun and opened my eyes to see a cow looking down at me, her snout nearly on my mouth. I gasped, but didn't leap up, just in case I would frighten her. This was not my idea of relaxation, fending off perverts and cows on an exotic beach. I picked up my belongings and walked toward the opposite end of the beach, where there were very few people. A middle-aged man approached me, encouraging me to come to his ayurvedic massage shack, where he and his wife were offering discounted services, since the main bulk of tourists had left for the season. I decided to take him for his word and get a much-needed massage. For all I knew, this would probably be the only relaxation I would get from now until the end of the trip. Eli was not the type of guy to handle pain and sickness very well. It was a shame that so many fell for his appearance before they grew to understand that he was really a complete asshole.

The masseuse gave me his card, and after an hour of bliss, I went to the room to check up on Eli. He had gotten even worse. He had managed to strip down to his underwear, and he was sweating and vomiting into a bucket on the side of the bed. Okay, so maybe I underestimated his sickness. I asked the owners to call for a rickshaw to take us to the nearest hospital. It turned out that there was a nearby ward about five minutes away by car. We drove up a long dirt road lined with foliage, curving in and out of weeds, until we found the main street. We made a turn and in a few minutes were in front of the Palolem Maternity Hospital.

Unfortunately the head—and only—doctor wasn't there. He was tending to business in the capital. All we had was a series of nurses in white robes and flip-flops to help us out in our dilemma. By then it was eight p.m., and the sun had just set. The nurses took Eli's temperature and offered him some water and a sedative. Outside, a light rain descended upon the beach town, and the hospital lights flickered as the winds blew at the building's fragile electric infrastructure. The head nurse called the doctor in, and we waited there in the emergency ward of this makeshift hospital for the doctor to arrive. As we sat waiting in the room, the lights dimmed in and out. After twenty minutes, the lights went out completely, and we were left sitting in the dark. The nurse came in with a flashlight and assured us that everything would be fine.

An hour later, the doctor arrived, and assessed that the bug Eli likely had was a bad case of food poisoning. It was made worse by the injury that Eli had sustained from being stabbed in the stomach while he was in Rikers. Though he was able to dance and workout, the area was still sensitive and prone to infection. The doctor urged him to take it easy and prescribed an antibacterial tablet for him, which he would have to pick up at the nearby pharmacy. Bleary-eyed, Eli stared at the doctor in confusion. It was clear that I would have to be his caregiver until he was coherent enough to make his own medical decisions.

A nurse volunteered to take us to the pharmacy in town, so that Eli could at least have some relief until the morning. We drove along in the rickshaw until we reached a small house hidden away deep in the bush. The rickshaw stopped.

"This is the pharmacist. She's closed now, but we can wake her to get the medicine," the nurse informed me. We knocked on the door. There was no answer. We continued knocking, until a weary middle-aged woman appeared at the door in sandals and a robe.

"What is it?" She seemed more tired than annoyed. The nurse spoke to her in a Hindi dialect. She nodded and closed the door a little and went to fetch a pair of walking shoes. She summoned us behind her as we walked to a building adjacent to her home. She opened the door with a key and we all stood together in the dark while the pharmacist searched for the light switch.

Finally finding the light cord, she pulled on the string in the dark, and the fluorescent light flooded the dark night. Almost instantly, a swarm of flies, attracted to the light, swarmed around us. She quickly found the medication and handed it to me. I paid her and we left, praying that this mystery medication would work, so we could be on our way. The nurse turned to us, but was giving me the directions, as Eli was clearly unavailable.

"Take this, and hopefully it will calm your upset stomach. It is probably a bacterial infection from the food you ate in Jaipur. If you don't feel better in the morning, come back to the hospital and we will reevaluate the situation." The nurse administered the tablet to Eli, and then we went back to the hotel room.

~

The following morning Eli was no better. We went back to the hospital, and the head doctor looked at us with dread. This was a maternity hospital and he delivered babies. The last thing he needed was a sickly American dying from an unknown infection on his watch. It was too much of a liability for a person whose life was relatively simple in this small jungle town where every minute activity landed in the paper.

"Still not better?" He took Eli to the office, where he felt around for lumps. Eli winced and cried out in pain every time the doctor pressed on his lower abdomen. This was serious. "I'm going to try one thing before our last resort. I will pass a tube through your nostril, down to your intestine, to help drain out the excess fluid that has accumulated in your stomach. If, after a day, it hasn't gotten better, we will go to the next step, which is to get a CT Scan to take a look at what is going on inside. If the situation is dire, we may need to prepare for surgery."

We certainly didn't want the surgery option so we agreed to go ahead with the doctor's suggestion. The nurses set up a room for Eli where he would be staying for a few days to be tested and evaluated.

There was no elevator to get to the second floor where Eli would be staying. Instead there were wide, steep ramps that led us to each floor. The nurses were busy with other patients and their flip-flops slapped loudly against the tiled ramps. Every now and then, we could hear the wail of a newborn baby, or the pained sighs of a woman in labor. I knew that Eli's situation was putting a strain on the small staff. Though there was supposed to be only one nurse per shift assigned to Eli, everyone was curious about the American patient, so it came to be that all nurses on staff attended to Eli in one way or another.

Luckily the room had an air conditioner, a television, and plenty of electrical outlets. This would at least keep Eli happy for the time he was there. He had brought his Playstation Portable, his iPod, an iPod dock, some DVDs, and plenty of snacks, books, and magazines to keep him occupied, just in case he got bored with India. Eli was a prince in a castle. Every twenty minutes he would call out for a nurse and they would come running. He mainly wanted ice, which was a real pain to get because the only freezer was in the basement, which was essentially three flights down. They all catered to him like loving servants, but the one thing he really wanted was a shower.

"I can't believe these people," he complained. "The nurses are horrible. I keep asking for ice, and they take forever to get me ice. And I need to bathe. I haven't bathed since I came here. These nurses keep giving me sponge baths. And this one nurse? She tried to wipe down my feet with the same washcloth that she washed my body with." I thought about his complaints, and realized that his feet hadn't come in contact with the ground at all that day.

"Can you at least help me to the shower? I need a shower. I need to bathe."

Unfortunately, he couldn't stand by himself without help, so I helped him in and out of the shower. In his helplessness, I actually took some pity on him and his situation, even though I hoped that this horrendous experience would teach him to be a little more appreciative of life and the people around him. I helped him dress, and get back into the bed. And then I left him in the room to go eat and refuel my senses. The nurses looked at me in panic as I walked out of the hospital.

"Where are you going?" they all asked frantically.

"Oh, I'll be back, I just need a break. I promise I'll be back by this evening." I needed a drink, some air, the beach, anything that wasn't related to Eli. I was so sick of him and his whining and compulsive behavior. I decided to walk up the street to try and find a shack to get something to eat. There was nothing for a mile in either direction, it seemed. The only things that were available were two shacks selling chips, soda, candy, and other dried goods. I was starving. I continued walking up the path and came across a lovely little bed and breakfast. There was a coconut tree out front, and two men were atop the trees knocking down the fruit for some of the dishes. I asked for one and they sliced open a fresh coconut for me to drink. I took out a book that I had been reading, and settled into one of the lounge chairs that lined the front of the establishment. On a table were some local newspapers that were thankfully written in English. I read up on the local news, and a waiter came out and offered me a menu, from which I ordered a light Mediterranean salad, and something called a lemon nana. It was a simple drink of lemon, crushed mint, raw sugar, and ice, but it completely made my day.

After my meal, I decided to take a chance and take a walk to the main city. I didn't think it was so far since it only took about five minutes in a rickshaw. It was a beautiful day, and I needed the time to be alone and gather my thoughts over the past day's events. I needed to get our things from the hotel room and bring them to the hospital, since we obviously were going to have to cut the trip short. An older nurse saw me walking back and agreed to walk with me. We walked along the winding roads and some pretty empty spaces. At one point a wild cow charged at me, and I freaked out, running until she got tired and stopped in her tracks. We laughed together at the incident. Suddenly every hiss and tick made me jump. I didn't know what kind of animal would try to get at me. But I kept walking until I made it into the city. I paid the hotel owners, packed our things into a rickshaw, and headed back to the hospital.

~

It was dark by now, and when I got back to the hospital, the lights were out. Frantic that I had gotten locked out, I tapped on the door. A nurse appeared and let me in.

"We turn out the lights at night. Too many bugs." She led me up the ramp to the floor where Eli was staying. I went into the room and dropped our belongings on the spare bed. Eli had been hooked up with a tube that ran through his nose to his stomach. In the bag was a smelly green substance. It was the ooze that was coming out of his intestines. His stomach pain seemed to be subsiding, but he still ached. The doctor checked in on him periodically until his shift was over.

"I'll check on your progress tomorrow. If it hasn't gotten better, then I will need to refer you to a specialist." I just sat in the spare bed, relaxing myself, as Eli squirmed in his bed beside me, complaining.

"Can you get the nurse? I've been ringing them but they haven't come back. I really need some ice." I walked outside the room looking for help. The hallways were pitch black, but I heard nurses whispering nearby. I ran my hand along the wall to find a light switch so that I wouldn't wind up tumbling down the ramps to the bottom level of the hospital. I finally found the switch and flicked on the light. To my horror, the light revealed a wall covered in mosquitoes, their stomachs red from the blood they managed to scavenge. Their little bodies quivered at the sharp blare of the lamp. A nurse ran out of the room quickly and shut off the light.

"Do you need something?" she asked me.

"Yes, ice. He needs ice." The nurse sighed. "Okay, I will get it." Before she ran off, I volunteered. Lord knows what kind of hell Eli had been subjecting those nurses to. I went back to the room with some ice and asked Eli if he wanted to call someone to let them know about his situation.

"Yeah, I'm gonna call my mom," he said. "My cell phone allows me to call direct." He called her and told her the news, assuring her that he would be all right. But he was too weary to explain the whole situation so I took the phone and laid it on her direct. I also was sure to let her know that I was footing the bill, since Eli was in no capacity to sign credit card slips or read invoices. Medical help was not free, even in a developing country. She assured me that they would take care of me once I got back, and that they would send money to the hospital to cover his costs.

~

The following day Eli appeared to have gotten worse, and

the doctor was at a loss as to what to do with his sickly American patient. It didn't help that Eli was a pain in the ass. He likely wouldn't mind if Eli just got up and left, with no record of his visit to the hospital. But to the doctor's disappointment, Eli wouldn't budge. The doctor approached Eli gravely.

"I'm afraid I don't have the capabilities to examine you here. You will need to go to the capital to get a professional CT scan. I just don't have that kind of machinery here."

I was annoyed. A part of me felt bad for Eli, but another part of me was pissed that this awful motherfucker had truly ruined my trip by being an asshole and getting sick. I contacted his mother, who in turn contacted his favorite aunt, Mimi. Mimi was a registered nurse, and apparently the family authority on any medical advice. I listened as she spoke slowly and repetitively.

"I've been a nurse for twenty-five years. Those people over there, they don't know what they're doing. Just get the scans and get on the first flight back home." I rolled my eyes as she spoke.

"Yes," I say, appeasing her, "I will be sure to make sure that he gets home as soon as possible. Right now, they are just trying to drain as much fluid out of his intestines, and when he gets well enough to walk, then we'll be able to get on the next flight." This was a partial truth. I didn't know if Eli would be able to get on a flight before the weekend, and honestly, I didn't want to pay a fee to change my airline ticket. It was he, after all, which was sick with an infection, not me. I was simply on vacation. It didn't help that Eli was an asshole, so I meant to expend as little energy as possible on this crazy man.

~

Eli and I took the two-hour ride with him up to the capital, Panaji, while the two surgeons crammed into the front seat. Once there, I waited in a hot and musty medical office while Eli got X-rays taken. After a few more hours, the surgeons reviewed the X-rays and concluded that Eli had gangrene and would need surgery. At this point I wanted to leave him. But then I thought about all the bad karma that might come back to me if I dared do such a thing. What if I were in the same situation? Would I want to be left alone to die in a developing country? Eli wasn't too happy at the surgeons' findings either. For once he shriveled behind his bravado. "I'm going to die here. I'm going to die in India."

"Oh, don't say that," I said, trying to comfort him. Let's just pray and hope there is an alternative." We took the trip back down to Palolem with the results. The surgeons followed us and had a long discussion with the head maternity doctor. He came out of his office with a stern look on his face. They approached me, since Eli was nauseous and had a fever.

"The gangrene has advanced, and it has caused a serious infection in his large intestine. We will need to operate very soon, or the infection will become much, much worse." It was up to Eli. He would need to decide what to do, and how to pay for the surgery if he decided to go through with it. At this point he could barely walk, let alone gather himself to get aboard a twelve-hour plane ride.

"Might I add," the doctor continued, "the airlines will not let you fly in your condition. And I cannot give you a note of good health to allow you to fly; I could lose my license." So these were Eli's options: fucked, or fucked and dead.

~

I seriously needed to get away from this nightmare. Nightfall was fast approaching. I was hungry, and, remembering the restaurants that lined the main road to the beach, I decided to venture back to the main part of town. As I set foot outside the hospital, I caught sight of a rickshaw, waiting to transport passengers at an inflated rate. Since Eli was admitted, I had been taking these rickshaws to get back and forth between the town and the hospital at night. I was sick of spending money and decided to walk alone, along the unlighted roads, to the center of town.

While Eli was sleeping, I decided to snatch his electric hand-lamp and bug repellent, which were buried deep in his bag full of every essential a spoiled Westerner could need. Going through his belongings, I came across a heap of tightly balled-up clothes. When I went to pick them up I was nearly sliced in two as a set of five serrated daggers, all shaped in various hook-like forms fell out of the heap. I gasped softly as I stared at the weapons and looked back at Eli, who was in a deep sleep. It was then that I knew his sudden illness was a Godsend. I took the smallest blade to keep for my own protection, quickly rewrapped the other knives, stuffed them back in the bag, found the lamp and repellent, and made my way down the hospital ramps to the door that would lead me to freedom from this psychotic man. One of the nurses saw me leaving and rushed over to me.

"Hey! Wait! I'm going too. Please. Walk with me." It was the youngest nurse, and she was eager to share the walk with me. She was holding a small, pen-like flashlight. Her voice was light and airy, like the whisper of a young girl. Her tone made her sound even more juvenile than her obvious inexperience as a nurse. Both of our lights glowed powerfully in the pitch-black jungle. I held the lamp low, so that I could see the ground. Occasionally, we would hear a rustle in the bush, and pitch our lamps in front of us to make sure we didn't mistakenly walk into or onto a beast.

"I walk home all the time. It's easy, but sometimes I like to walk with somebody." Strangely, in the darkness of the Goan jungle, I felt safe. The wild flora surrounded us as we walked down the narrow path to the main fork. The hisses and distant barks of stray dogs hardly fazed me, and an occasional buzz in my ear from a mosquito barely threw me off-guard. I had somehow grown accustomed to the natural heartbeat of the jungle. As we rounded the corner toward the main drag of the city, the nurse parted and went to her small hut, walking off a dirt path into the night's darkness.

I kept walking, toward the street filled with the tourist restaurants, and came across some thumping music from behind a thicket of palms. I saw a group of Europeans dancing in front of a charming two-story cement house. The doors were colored a bright shade of blue from what I could make out, and tea lights were strung from tree to tree making an intimate glow in the yard. I could smell the faint aroma of ganja and citronella burning, and the smoky embers of a barbecue. Suddenly, a man pulled up behind me on his moped. He was a southern California type, complete with dirty-blonde hair and surfer body to match.

"Hey, what's up? I'm Tyler. You visiting?"

"Oh yes," I said, taken aback from this man's easy friendliness. "Well actually, I was on vacation and my friend is in the hospital. He got an infection and he'll probably have surgery."

"Oh shit, that sucks. Where are you guys from?"

"America. New York—Brooklyn, actually."

"Well, why don't you come in and have some beer and chill out. I can only imagine how nerve-wracked you are." It seemed silly to be walking into some stranger's yard in a foreign country at night, though I had done similar things so many times in my travels. I had always seemed to ignore the very basic childhood advice of never walking off with strangers. For some reason, as an adult, I felt immune from something awful happening to me. Of course, carrying a blade helped to boost my confidence. Anything could have happened to me in those forests, and nobody would know where to find me, but something about the scenario just felt so natural. The house was a wonderfully airy space, painted a deep, tropical blue. The windows of the home were large and arched, and the doorways were wonderfully carved in tradition-al South-Indian style. The small courtyard was filled with color-ful flora from what I could make out in the night, and glowing candles sat inside colorful glasshouses that hung above us, strung among the palm trees. The deep scent of weed and citronella was stronger now, and through the haze of smoke, I made out a mid-dle-aged couple sitting in hammocks in front of the house. Next to them was a young girl, possibly my age, dancing alongside her dog, smoking a joint.

"Hi there, I'm Marie, and this is my husband, Bill." I in-troduced myself.

"Are you here on holiday?"

"Yeah . . . well. I was on holiday, until my travel partner got sick. He's in the hospital now." The group gasped.

"Palolem Hospital? Isn't that a maternity hospital?" The girl with the dog asked. "I'm Amy by the way." She got up and gave me a hug. I was disarmed by their welcoming nature and sat down in their cipher. Amy passed me the joint and I took a drag off the wonderfully fragrant and fresh-tasting herb.

"Yeah," I continued. "We were in Jaipur and he got sick after we ate at this fancy restaurant. And he's been acting like a complete bitch this whole trip, and I'm really just done with him." As I spoke, I felt my body tense up with anger and aggravation. Amy rubbed my back as I took a long drag on the joint and inhaled deeply. I passed the joint to Tyler. "So now we're in Goa, and we tried to see if the sickness would go away, but he just hasn't gotten better."

"Well, I'm glad you found us. We were just having a little barbecue and some drinks. Would you care for a beer?" Amy pulled an ice -cold Kingfisher from a cooler and handed it to me. I could smell some chicken and roasting corn. It was a welcome reprieve from all of the thoroughly Indian dishes I had been eating for the past two weeks. As I grabbed some food and settled into a hammock to enjoy my meal I could hear a faint muffled cry. When I saw that no one else was bothered I sat back and started eating. Then I heard another thud.

"Okay, what is that?" I asked.

"Oh that's just James," Bill, the Englishman replied, nonchalantly. He took a slow drag off his joint and then passed it to his wife. They sat contentedly, sipping beers, and staring into the night as the man cried and pounded on a door somewhere in the house.

"Okay, well where is he?" I asked, incredulously. The thuds were getting louder.

"He's inside coming off his high, Marie answered. "He likes to take dog tranquilizers and Monkey Gin together." She rolled her eyes and got up to open the front door.

"Please," the man pleaded, in what seemed a Scottish accent. "Please let me out."

"James!" Marie screamed. The man appeared to be locked in a room inside the house. She went into the house and peered at him through a peephole in the door to his room. "Calm down! Listen, James, we can't let you out. You might hurt yourself. And if you hurt yourself, we could get in trouble, do you understand?"

"No, I won't hurt myself! I promise. Just please let me out. I'm claustrophobic." Marie slowly opened the door, and a diminutive blond-haired man hopped out of the darkness, giggling. He wore glasses and appeared disheveled, but otherwise completely normal. I had pictured a scruffy-looking derelict. He saw me sitting quietly and frantically waved.

"Where are you from?"

"America. Brooklyn, to be exact." I shook his hand. "Nice to meet you." He went over to the cooler to grab a beer. Tyler passed him the joint, but James refused.

"Oh, I don't do that stuff. Totally fucks me up, you know? And it smells." I laughed at the irony of James' statement. It was a cool setup, this little house sitting on the beach. Marie and her husband seemed so carefree and at ease. And I couldn't help but ponder the thought of living the simple life in the Goan forest.

"Is it expensive to live here?" I asked Marie.

"Oh no, not at all. We paid what would amount to $800 a month in rent for this entire house. We make the money back and then some, in one night during the high season. The bulk of our income comes from British tourists. They come here and splash money around like it's going out of style."

"The place that we were renting before my friend went in the hospital was only four-hundred rupees a night. I thought we had a great deal since it's a little off-season."

"Have you been staying there alone?"

"Actually I moved our stuff out of the hotel and brought it to the hospital. The hospital is free, for me at least, and you can't beat that!"

"Well, you are welcome to stay with us for a night or two," Marie offered, you know—if you need to get away from the hospital scene."

"And there's always plenty of weed," Tyler interjected. We all laughed and smoked and drank until the lights of the village dimmed, one by one, and all we could hear were the sounds of the crickets singing in the hot jungle.

~

Before it got too late, I made my way back to the hospital. Spending the night there was more a welcome luxury than an inconvenience. Thanks to Eli's prissiness, and the fact that he was extremely ill, the doctors allowed him to periodically run the air conditioning, and the bathroom was cleaned daily. I only occasionally shared my daily shower with a wandering iguana. The staff was excellent at feeding Eli, and since he was a vegan preparing for surgery, his meals were relatively simple. They bathed him twice every day, but even so, he insisted on having me give him an additional bath because he hated how they used the same washcloth to clean his face and wipe his body. The room was sparse, but the linens were constantly changed, and Eli, to his utter enjoyment, had the pleasure of a satellite TV for entertainment. We kept the windows closed to keep the room cool, but Eli being the sissy that he was, suddenly insisted on leaving the bathroom light on. Fear had finally hit him. The nurses had us keep the bathroom window open for circulation, which unfortunately allowed mosquitos and other wild creatures to enter the bathroom. Luckily I had brought along my mosquito net and covered the bathroom window, but somehow a few geckos always managed to find their way into the bathroom sink. I welcomed the little guests as I bathed. They were a playful distraction from the terror of the man that lay beyond the bathroom doors.

The nurses came in the following night to give him his usual sponge bath before bed. I dressed hurriedly, trying to make my way out of the hospital before he could have the chance to ask me to give him an additional bath, but I was a minute too slow. As the nurses worked quickly, changing his clothing and sheets, Eli caught sight of me, and rolling over feebly, asked me to bathe him once again.

"Please?"

"But Eli, that's what the nurses are for. You do know that you're paying them for this, right?"

"But you would do it better because you know how I like to be bathed."

If this is what it was like to have kids, I didn't want one anytime soon. I sighed and waited for the nurses to leave the room before bathing Eli. As I rubbed him down with shea butter I watched him fall slowly asleep, with the glow of an Indian soap opera illuminating the room.

~

When Eli woke, he asked me to call his aunt Mimi, with whom he trusted his soul. For some reason, he believed that she had all the answers. After a series of yeahs, and uh-huhs, he handed me the phone, even after I emphatically waved my hands expressing that I did not need to speak to her. He thrusted the phone in my hands.

"Hi. I want to thank you again for watching over Eli. You are truly an angel."

"Thank you," I replied. I walked out of the hospital room into an empty office across the hall, while still on the line.

"Listen, I want you to do all that you can to stall the doctors. Just get him on the plane. The last thing we can trust are some doctors in the middle of nowhere." I sighed outside the range of the receiver. "What have they said?"

"Well, the outlook is not so good. The scans show an advancement of the infection. I think at this point that the surgery is inevitable. The doctor could let Eli go, but he refuses to give him a bill of good health to fly. Eli can barely walk. He's in severe pain."

"DO NOT let them cut him open. Don't let them touch him!"

"But they really are doing the best they can, and Eli does not look very good at all. This is really a life-or-death situation, but we have to trust that these doctors know what they are doing. The surgeons who would be doing the operation are some of the best in the state, and they will be coming all the way from the capital to do this operation. It's really a big deal."

"Listen, I'm a nurse. I've been doing this for 25 years, I know what I'm talking about," she repeated to me, for about the twentieth time. I replied in agreement, at her redundancy, while rolling my eyes at her foolishness. She made it a point to remind me of this every time I spoke to her, as if I would not remember. I was annoyed and tired. She cajoled, threatened, cried, talked, and ranted to me about what I needed to do, and what she would do to the staff if they didn't follow her orders. And what the fuck, exactly, was she going to do twenty thousand miles away on the other side of the world? "We could airlift him out. I've seen them do that." Yeah, I thought, and do YOU have the money to airlift him? This lady's scope of unrealistic expectations was pissing me off, and I just wanted to get off the phone and go smoke a joint with my new friends by the beach. Her words were a blur of nonsense as I thought about how lovely it would feel to hold that thin coil of freshly dried herb between my lips while I sipped on a beer and stared up between the palm trees into the star-lit sky.

~

The doctors arrived early that morning to prepare for the surgery. I had full confidence in the surgeons, but Eli was positive he would die. He would have preferred to die in America, but for once, he didn't have a say in the matter, and relinquished his power to everyone around him. The nurses transferred him to the surgery bed and wheeled him down the two levels of indoor ramps that led to the surgery. I held his hand as we went through the doors, and he smiled. For that fleeting moment, I felt a bit of compassion for a man that I had loathed the entire time. Best-case scenario would be that he comes out of this surgery sealed up and ready to heal. Worst case? I didn't dare think about it. The surgery would only be about two hours, the doctor assured me. I left the hospital to go have breakfast at the nearby shack that had become my new place of respite.

Since Goa was likely to be the last place in India that I would get to visit before we went home to New York, I resolved to purchase whatever gifts and trinkets I could in the town and at the shack. Some authentic chai here, a little necklace there. The locals had come to know me well as I was the only black woman around town, so they bargained less with me because they figured I would return later. As I sipped my lemon nana at the shack, I thought about everything that had happened and why it was likely for the better. Throughout the trip, Eli's unstable behavior had become increasingly agitated. It came to a head in the Jaipur hotel. Maybe his sickness was my saving grace from a possibly fatal future with him in an Indian city. I said a prayer and headed back to the hospital to check on Eli's status.

I walked into the hospital, and for the first time noticed the list of patients hanging on a white sheet of paper on the wall near the door. On the left-hand side were the names of the patients, mostly women in pre- and post-labor, with a few sprinklings of locals with various injuries like a broken foot or hand burn. The nurses offered me a seat just outside the doors that lead to surgery, and I sat, reading a book. About twenty minutes later one of the surgeons came out to give me an update on Eli. The woman came up to the doors and instructed me to come in. She held a silver bowl in her hands and what lay inside was a green tube of bloodied intestine the thickness of my forearm. The wretched smell filled the waiting room, and I nearly vomited in my mouth. I gawked at the obscenity, and then took a picture of it, for posterity. The surgeon went back into the operating room to close Eli up and complete the task. I needed a drink.

On my way back to the center of town, I saw Amy on a moped, waved to her, and caught a ride. She swerved on and off the bumpy dirt roads, avoiding the small pits where the locals lit their trash on fire.

"I was fermenting some cheese. I actually just finished a batch. Would you like to try some when we get back to my place?" The thought of eating homemade cheese in Goa, of all places, made me laugh.

"But how do you store this cheese? Isn't refrigeration expensive here?"

"My parents, as a parting gift, offered to get me the refrigerator and cheese-making tools so that I could practice my craft. My grandmother used to make her own cheese. I was never into it until recently, after my boyfriend killed himself." I was silent. She drove the moped underneath some large palms, and onto a dark road where there were a few small shacks. "This is where I stay." We got out and went inside the small apartment.

"I'm sorry about your boyfriend. How long ago did this happen?"

"Two years ago. The authorities called me. They found him hanging in a tree, somewhere in the bush. He maybe was a little high." She spoke in a monotonous tone, seemingly removed from the graphic detail of her boyfriend's death that she had just narrated. "But my parents gave me a new lease on life. My mom purchased this refrigerator for me and she taught me the basics of making cheese. Would you like to try some?" She reached into the refrigerated bin and pulled out a square crème-colored piece of cheese. The taste was very sharp and slightly chalky, but not altogether bad. It reminded me of a softer version of a well-aged Parmesan.

"It's not bad," I replied. "May I have some to take home with me?"

"Of course. And maybe, if it's good enough, I can send you some more. I've always wanted to visit America." I nodded even though I knew the prospect of this young hippy girl living in India making her way across the Atlantic Ocean to my little

Brooklyn apartment anytime soon was slight. Still, it was always a good idea to be hospitable, since I never knew if I would meet her again, in another place at some other time. We took a few more drags of the joint before leaving her hut and heading back to the British couple's house where we smoked herb and told stories deep into the night.

~

The next day the head doctor came in to check on Eli's progress. I could hear the wail of babies in the nearby rooms, but the talk of all the hospital was the miracle surgery on the annoying American. Even though the surgery went well, he had urged Eli to stay another week to fully recover. For me, that was not an option, as I was nearly out of funds, and my patience was wearing thin from a vacation gone horribly wrong.

"Is there any way that we can just go, if he is at least able to walk around?" I pleaded. Eli was more enthusiastic than ever to leave the country.

"I want to go home to America, where the hospitals are clean and I can get real care," Eli blurted. I shot him a murderous glare.

"Eli, these people just saved your life. They are doing the best they can."

"Well, I didn't want to have surgery in the first place." The doctor interjected.

"May I remind you that even if you were to fly home, you might not have made it for the entire flight? Your sickness was in an advanced state. You are lucky you came to us when you did, or else the circumstances would have been very grave." The doctor said these words without a hint of anger or pity. "Why don't you rest a bit, call your relatives and let them know you are okay." Eli agreed, and we left him alone, happy in his room, with the TV, iPod, and video game console.

~

It was day two after the surgery and I grew antsier by the minute. Our tickets were set for three days from then, and if Eli wasn't able to fly, I was prepared to leave him there.

"Please don't leave him there with those people," his aunt Mimi pleaded. "You've done such a great job, and you are the only one we have to make sure Eli is okay. We need you." Her voice was strained over the tinny cell phone connection. As I sat on the edge of Eli's bed, I looked worriedly at his incision, covered with tape and endlessly oozing blood and pus. Whenever he moved the wrong way a seam from his stapled stomach would burst, drenching the surgical dressings, and sending searing pain through Eli's abdomen. Eli could barely move without assistance. I couldn't picture him making it on an airplane.

"How do you feel today?" The doctor asked.

"I feel like I want to go home," Eli grunted. The doctor laughed at the absurd comment.

"You just came out of major surgery. There is no way you can go home in your condition." His last comment made me uneasy. After this ordeal, I was ready to go home, and could not bear the expense or the headache of staying a minute longer with this lunatic. I knew I could have left at any moment, but for some reason my empathetic side reasoned that Eli needed someone to be by his side, and I would want the same if I were in his situation.

"Listen doc, how soon can I get out of here?" Eli asked, annoyed.

"To be honest, I can't give you a good bill of health to fly. I could lose my license." Eli shuffled uneasily in his bed. "As I said, you need to stay here at least another week to recover."

"Hell no, I am not staying here for another week. I'm going home to civilization," Eli barked defiantly. The doctor sighed and left the room. He had had enough of Eli, but there was nothing he could do short of throwing the man out on the street and so losing his license and livelihood. I followed the doctor down the ramps to his office. Eli was being a total asshole, and I was the only voice of reason to the hard-working Indian staff. I knocked on his office door.

"Come in." I walked in and sat humbly in his office chair.

"Listen, I want to apologize for my friend's behavior." I thought about how the word friend sounded on my lips when referring to Eli. He wasn't a friend, and I was ashamed that he wasn't even my acquaintance. The doctor was sympathetic.

"We know that you are not like him, and you cannot take responsibility for his behavior. We have all done our best, and we thank you for mediating between us. It has been very difficult, and I took a huge risk. I am a maternity doctor. I deliver babies. I didn't have to take on your friend."

"Yes, I know, I know. And I thank you. Your team has been incredible, but it has been difficult for me as well. Eli's family wants me to get him home as soon as possible. And then I have Eli whining in my ear constantly. I am worn out and I can't take it any longer." The doctor nodded. "There is only one thing I can do. He can leave this hospital without being discharged, of his own accord. I cannot give him a clean bill of health, however, for purposes of flying back home. So you risk the chance that the airline will not let him fly. If you are willing to take that chance, you can leave whenever you want."

"Okay, doctor. Thank you. Thank you so much." I left his office and went back to Eli's room to tell him the news.

"Great! Let's leave tomorrow!" Eli popped up in his bed and then jerked his body down as the surgical cut tore apart and a stream of pus and blood streamed out of the staples in his belly. He cried out and a nurse ran in to change the surgical dressings. "Can you call my mom?" I called her and told her the news.

"Our flight is in two days. We'll leave out extra early to give us enough time and then once we get to Mumbai it should be a smooth ride, unless the authorities prohibit Eli from flying."

"Oh thank God," his mother exclaimed. "This nightmare

is almost over."

"You're telling me."

~

I walked back into town to say good-bye to my new friends, and to grab a few snacks and trinkets. As I was purchasing a set of beach-themed lighters from a newsstand I overheard a group of locals shouting frantically.

"No! Sir! Please!" There was a wave of screams.

"This way! Stop!" A crowd of people scurried from side to side on the sand road that led to the main beach. I saw a white bespectacled man swerving precariously on a moped. It was James.

"James!" I shouted. "Hey James! What the hell are you doing?" I laughed. He didn't recognize me, but the locals looked at me angrily as if I were responsible for this drunken man nearly running over their shops. I stepped back and waved my hands in a "no-no" gesture.

"Oh no, I don't *know* him." I looked on at the hapless man and wondered where his friends, the British couple, were. I left the chaotic scene to find their house and found Marie there, gardening.

"Hey there! Where is everyone?"

"Oh, they went into the central city today. Had some business to attend to. What are you up to today?"

"Oh, I'm actually leaving and just wanted to say goodbye. Do you know, I just saw James by the beach? He was on a moped and he nearly ran over all the shops!"

"Ah that James, we had to let him go. We couldn't contain him. I think there's no going back with that guy. We tried to help him, but we think it's best for the authorities to deal with him. He's a liability, and we have a business to run.

"I understand." I reached out to give Marie a hug. "I'm so glad I found you guys here in this village. There is no way I would have stayed sane without you."

"Glad to be of service. Listen, here is my card. Keep in touch, okay?"

"I will, I will," I said, as I walked off outside the town for the last time.

~

The cab arrived early in the morning and the nurses made sure that all of Eli's belongings were packed and that he was dressed as simply and cleanly as possible. The doctor gave him several sets of dressings to change as needed and urged him not to make any sudden or sharp movements, and one wrong move could split his stomach wide open in the airplane aisle. As we piled our belongings into the car, I ran back and gave every single one of the staff a hug and took a picture for posterity. I couldn't thank them enough. Eli barely waved a good-bye as he sat comfortably in the air-conditioned car.

~

The day was bright and cheerfully sunny, and I sat in silence observing the natural surroundings along the uninhabited road.

"Excuse me," Eli tapped the cab driver on the shoulder. "I need to go to the bank. I'm really low on cash."

"But we're going to the airport. I'm sure you have enough for some snacks there. Why take out money now?" I tried to reason with the man. Eli just looked at me, annoyed.

"It's my money and I want it." The cab driver found the nearest bank in town and we waited and watched as Eli withdrew an obscene amount of money from the ATM. When he returned to the car, I looked at him incredulously.

"Why would you take out so much money?" I asked.

"Because I have it to take. Besides, it will be a nice souvenir." I shook my head as the driver pulled off onto the main road to the airport.

~

"Can we turn off the AC and roll down the windows?" I asked. Eli surprisingly agreed, and he rolled down his window and stuck his hand out to grab a branch of a tree flush with leaves.

"Stop!" he shouted to the driver. "Can you please stop? I want that tree!"

"Eli, you're bugging. You cannot take a tree back with you to the States. Immigration will seize it."

"No, they won't. It's just a tree. Driver, please, can you stop? I want a tree!" I rolled my eyes in annoyance, and the driver looked back at me incredulously. "That one over there. Can you help me pull it up?"

"I'm not helping you. It's a silly thing to do." I pouted.

"Whatever." Eli looked to the driver. "Can you help me pick up the small one? It shouldn't be too hard, it's small!" The driver pulled and tugged at the little shrub until it was uprooted along with a huge lump of red clay. I couldn't believe this fuck-tard planned on trying to get a foreign tree through United States customs. I just shook my head, and nodded to sleep as the Indian driver helped Eli dig up the plant and transport it to the car.

~

"Where is your ticket?" We were in the Mumbai airport and the customs officer was prodding Eli. He couldn't find it. For all of our mini-trips I maintained all of our traveling arrangements including tickets, but Eli was responsible for the main ticket in and out of India.

"Didn't you print it out? I told you to print a copy of your tickets before you left home," I scolded him.

"But it's an e-ticket. I shouldn't need to print anything," Eli rationalized. I rolled my eyes and walked off towards the check-in line, while Eli rolled around looking for an Internet café in the airport terminal in order to print out his ticket. When Eli finally got his shit together, he found me, and I pushed him and his belongings in line toward the check-in desk. Luckily an airport employee saw me struggling and offered us assistance with the bags. I thanked him profusely, but Eli gave him a look of disgust.

"That's his job, I don't know why you're thanking him," Eli said nonchalantly. This final comment sent me over the edge. I pushed his wheelchair toward the gate and let go so that he bumped violently into the metal detector. As he fumbled for his travel documents, I quickly produced mine for the security agent, and he waved me through the gate.

"Miss, is he with you?" a guard asked.

"No, I'm not responsible for him," I replied nonchalantly. I turned around and saw Eli explaining to the guard why, exactly, he was bringing a tree back to the United States, and what his intentions were for the plant. I shook my head in annoyance and headed to the gate. An airline employee wheeled him behind me, but I quickened my pace to avoid being associated with the madness. Behind me I could hear him complaining about how badly the employee was steering him in his wheelchair. When he got to the gate, he demanded a bottle of water from the stewardess. I sat in the next section of seats, adjacent to the fool. I didn't want too many people to know that I knew this crazy dude, let alone traveled for a month with him.

As soon as we were settled on the plane, I immediately began to tally up the amount of money that he owed me. Not once on this horrific leg of the trip did he ever thank me for staying with him through these unfortunate events. I handed him the tab and he paid me cash on the spot.

"I can't wait to get home. India was such a hellhole. As soon as I get home, I'm having some of my momma's cooking. I'm sick of Indian food." He called his mother using his cell phone. By now the bill had to be several hundred dollars from all the calls he was making to the States. He didn't care; someone would pick up the tab once he got home. He told his mother the flight details and gate number. I could hear her through the phone, overjoyed that her baby was coming home. He hung up the phone, elated.

"Well, I made arrangements for getting home. My mom and cousin will be at the airport to pick me up and take me directly to the hospital. I'm not sure how you're gonna get home though."

"I'll work it out" I replied. I burned inside, and turned my body to face the window as angry tears streamed down my face. After everything we just went through, this selfish, self-absorbed son of a bitch couldn't even offer me a damn ride? It took everything in me to keep from going off on this motherfucker and causing a flight delay. I just took deep breaths, knowing that the universe would serve him his retribution, just as it kept doing every time he blessed someone with his shitty behavior.

~

The next day when we landed in New York, his mother ran out and hugged her son, and then she hugged me for a long time and offered her thanks. I could feel that she was trying to make up for the lack of kindness that her son offered me. I wondered where she went wrong in his upbringing, and for a moment, I hated all mommas' boys. These mothers, who constantly cater to the whims of their sons, feeding them, cleaning up after them, washing their clothes, paying their bills—were not raising men; they were raising grown-up boys who had no concept of chivalry, manhood, or responsibility. These were the boys who would later go out into the world looking for wives to do the same, and would always come back, bitter, to their mommas for comfort. The thought sent an angry shiver down my spine. After they dropped him off at the nearest hospital in New York City, his mother and cousin gave me a ride home. His mother turned to look at me.

"I can't believe you stayed with him. I would have left him there. I know how he is." I was shocked that these pearls of wisdom could come from a man's own mother. Maybe Eli really was just a bad seed. "He's just such a fuck-up sometimes, and he drains the hell out of me and everyone around him. Listen, if there is anything you need, you call me, understand?" When I finally made it home, I fell into a deep, long sleep. Ironically, I needed a vacation.

~

I had returned home from India a bit of a wreck. Eli was still in recovery, and he was calling me nearly every day for comfort. He had moved in to his mother's house temporarily so that he could recover with the help of a loved one. Apparently he had pissed off his entire family, raising hell, and spending absurd amounts of money, so that only his mother would tend to his erratic behavior. I had been his only friend, and I took the time to prepare some vegan soul food for the poor bastard, even though he didn't deserve it. I always believed that good deeds attracted good karma.

Several months later Eli had gotten himself into trouble again. He had been accused of assault with a deadly weapon, and this time the judge wasn't so lenient because his victim died a few days later. The district attorney was willing to give him a lighter plea deal, but Eli insisted on boasting of his martial arts expertise, so that he appeared as if he were a danger to society. The judge was not impressed and neither was the jury of public opinion. Angry comments from former lovers and associates filled the comments section of the *New York Daily News*. Eli was sent back to Rikers for life.

SANITY

Through all of the madness, dance kept me sane. I began taking class again at my enclaves in Harlem and Brooklyn, but eventually got up the nerve to visit my old studio downtown. I really had no desire to be around that group of women. Something about them brought out the most ugly and virulent parts of my character, and I had decided that I no longer wanted to be that kind of person. I felt bad for the women who were still dating him, and angry for how he felt no remorse for upending so many of these women's lives. He was an addiction; a gift and a curse wrapped in one, a God to many but a leader of none. So many times, I thought I had come so close to falling off a cliff with him, but I thanked God that I was sane enough to get out when I could. He no longer wanted me, and had grown to disdain me with such a deep aversion that one would have never known that we were once passionate lovers. His hatred of me was a blessing in disguise. My interactions with Abdoulaye were few and far between. It was always the same story with him. A new female teacher would arrive. He would comment on her looks to me, in a way that would make me feel angry and jealous. He knew that I knew that he was fucking her. I would roll my eyes and walk off in a huff. I was so sick of that shit. Why was I in this relationship?

Eventually, I had decided to take a hiatus from African dancing altogether and concentrate more on samba. I welcomed the Afro-Brazilian rhythms and movement, and the classes were devoid of the drama that accompanied the Senegalese and Guinean classes. Unlike the dancers who came out of the African dance classes, the women from the other classes always left swiftly. They had lives outside of dance class.

~

Every now and then I think of Abdoulaye, and my heart dips, just a little. And then an anger flows throughout my body. I think about the hundreds of people he defrauded, the countless lies he told, and the path of destruction he laid for so many lives No longer, my God, was he a cheap imitation, a facsimile thereof, a charlatan, and antichrist, unworthy of the adulation mistakenly poured upon him. I detested him with my entire soul.

I think about the Tristans, the Binhos, the Folas, and all of the other loves of my life. Each one brought something different to my life and I don't regret knowing any of them, regardless of their outcomes. I think about my travels from continent to continent, and how, after so many lovers, I would always come back to Him, and then to dance--my two loves that I sometimes hated. But I didn't hate dance so much as I hated the routine that it had become. The beauty of dance was always there. Whenever I rub my bare feet on a wooden floor, I think of Abdoulaye and of dance. Now it was time to separate the two entities that were once entwined.

~

We invest so much into what we love, oftentimes with dismal returns. It's funny how one can search the world for that perfect experience, and wind up having the experience of a lifetime right at home. Sometimes, I begin to turn my head and look back at what I may have lost, but unlike Lot's wife who turns into a pillar of salt when looking back on her burning city, I force myself to keep looking forward, pressing on. I live, learn, love, and travel.

Right now, I am researching tickets online. I am taking out my credit card. I am entering the details of my itinerary. I am pressing PURCHASE TICKET NOW, and once again, I am on my way.